Timed Subtraction Facts

Drills Improve Speed and Accuracy

Grades 1-3

Written by Ruth Solski
Illustrated by S&S Learning Materials

About the author:
Ruth Solski was an educator for 30 years. Ruth has written many educational resources over the years and is the founder of S&S Learning Materials. As a writer, her main goal is to provide teachers with a useful tool that they can implement in their classrooms to bring the joy of learning to children.

ISBN 978-1-55035-897-1
Copyright 2008
All Rights Reserved * Printed in Canada

Published in the United States by:
On The Mark Press
3909 Witmer Road PMB 175
Niagara Falls, New York
14305
www.onthemarkpress.com

Published in Canada by:
S&S Learning Materials
15 Dairy Avenue
Napanee, Ontario
K7R 1M4
www.sslearning.com

At A Glance

Learning Expectations	Pages 4 to 6	Pages 7 to 10	Pages 11 to 14	Pages 15 to 18	Pages 19 to 22	Pages 23 to 24	Pages 25 to 28	Pages 29 to 32	Pages 33 to 36	Pages 37 to 40	Pages 41 to 42	Pages 43 to 46
Subtraction Facts												
• To strengthen subtraction fact recall	•	•	•	•	•	•	•	•	•	•	•	•
• Improve speed and accuracy in subtraction facts	•	•	•	•	•	•	•	•	•	•	•	•
• Develop the ability to memorize	•	•	•	•	•	•	•	•	•	•	•	•
Timed Drills												
• Minus Zero, Minus One	•											
• Minus Two		•										
• Minus Three			•									
• Minus Four				•								
• Minus Five					•							
• Minus Zero to Minus Five Reviews						•						
• Minus Six							•					
• Minus Seven								•				
• Minus Eight									•			
• Minus Nine										•		
• Minus Six to Minus Nine Review											•	
• Subtraction Review Drills 0 to 18												•

Timed Subtraction Facts
Drills Improve Speed and Accuracy

Table of Contents

A Note to the Teacher:

The subtraction fact drills have been designated to help strengthen students' speed and accuracy through practice during a specified time or each student could be timed individually. This practice will help to strengthen the process of memorization which is a skill needed to recall facts quickly.

Some of the drills are shorter and are to be completed on a specified day. Each drill page concentrates on a specific area in subtraction fact recall. The drills proceed from the easiest level to the most difficult level. Each level has a daily practice page, a home practice page, an extra practice page, and a review test page.

The daily practice page is divided into five days. Each day of the week the student is to complete a drill. The date, score, and time it took are to be recorded in each section. This page could be glued into the students' workbooks or kept in individual file folders.

The home practice page is to be sent home to practice fact recall with parent supervision. Once completed it is to be returned to school and signed by a parent. A letter of explanation should be sent home with the first practice page explaining how it is to be completed.

The extra practice drill sheet is to be used with students who are still having difficulty recalling facts quickly and accurately. It is a different approach to the timed drill method. The student must supply the missing number. There is no extra practice page for minus zero and minus one subtraction facts.

The review page or test page is to be used to test the speed and accuracy within a given length of time. Begin with five minutes graduating down to one minute. Tell students when to begin and when to stop. Have the student circle the last completed question with a red crayon or a red pencil crayon. The students are to exchange their papers and to mark each incorrect answer with a red dot as you read the answers aloud. Have the students count the number of correct answers. No credit is to be given to incomplete answers. Record the number of correct answers, the time, and the date on each sheet where indicated. On each review test have all incomplete answers finished for extra practice.

There are two timed review tests for each section that may be used after each section has been practiced successfully. These tests will evaluate students' speed and accuracy in each section.

The final drill pages test all the facts from 0 to 18. These are to be used in the same manner as the other drills.

The results of the various drills may be recorded on the Score Record Sheets provided in the book.

Minus Zero, Minus One Drills

Name: _____

Date: Monday _____ Score: _____ /25   Time: _____ Min. _____ Sec.

6 – 1 = ____	12 – 1 = ____	8 – 1 = ____	6 – 1 = ____	5 – 1 = ____
10 – 1 = ____	7 – 1 = ____	13 – 1 = ____	3 – 1 = ____	10 – 0 = ____
9 – 1 = ____	2 – 1 = ____	9 – 0 = ____	4 – 0 = ____	9 – 1 = ____
5 – 0 = ____	4 – 1 = ____	5 – 1 = ____	2 – 1 = ____	14 – 1 = ____
3 – 1 = ____	6 – 0 = ____	10 – 1 = ____	7 – 0 = ____	8 – 1 = ____

Date: Tuesday _____ Score: _____ /25   Time: _____ Min. _____ Sec.

6 – 1 = ____	7 – 1 = ____	5 – 0 = ____	2 – 1 = ____	9 – 1 = ____
9 – 1 = ____	3 – 0 = ____	9 – 1 = ____	8 – 0 = ____	2 – 0 = ____
5 – 0 = ____	8 – 1 = ____	6 – 1 = ____	13 – 1 = ____	8 – 1 = ____
2 – 1 = ____	12 – 1 = ____	7 – 0 = ____	3 – 1 = ____	6 – 0 = ____
4 – 1 = ____	10 – 1 = ____	4 – 1 = ____	10 – 1 = ____	3 – 1 = ____

Date: Wednesday _____ Score: _____ /25   Time: _____ Min. _____ Sec.

4 – 0 = ____	3 – 1 = ____	2 – 0 = ____	8 – 1 = ____	4 – 1 = ____
7 – 1 = ____	10 – 1 = ____	7 – 1 = ____	5 – 1 = ____	2 – 1 = ____
2 – 1 = ____	9 – 1 = ____	4 – 1 = ____	9 – 0 = ____	7 – 0 = ____
8 – 0 = ____	5 – 1 = ____	3 – 0 = ____	10 – 1 = ____	8 – 1 = ____
6 – 1 = ____	1 – 1 = ____	6 – 1 = ____	11 – 1 = ____	3 – 0 = ____

Date: Thursday _____ Score: _____ /25   Time: _____ Min. _____ Sec.

9 – 1 = ____	6 – 0 = ____	3 – 1 = ____	6 – 1 = ____	8 – 1 = ____
8 – 1 = ____	4 – 1 = ____	7 – 1 = ____	2 – 1 = ____	3 – 1 = ____
10 – 1 = ____	2 – 1 = ____	17 – 1 = ____	5 – 1 = ____	10 – 1 = ____
16 – 1 = ____	5 – 1 = ____	10 – 1 = ____	9 – 1 = ____	18 – 1 = ____
7 – 1 = ____	9 – 0 = ____	8 – 0 = ____	4 – 0 = ____	7 – 0 = ____

Date: Friday _____ Score: _____ /25   Time: _____ Min. _____ Sec.

4 – 1 = ____	2 – 0 = ____	4 – 1 = ____	2 – 1 = ____	5 – 1 = ____
3 – 1 = ____	18 – 1 = ____	3 – 1 = ____	15 – 1 = ____	3 – 1 = ____
6 – 0 = ____	9 – 1 = ____	5 – 1 = ____	7 – 0 = ____	4 – 0 = ____
5 – 1 = ____	10 – 0 = ____	6 – 0 = ____	8 – 1 = ____	2 – 1 = ____
7 – 1 = ____	8 – 1 = ____	9 – 1 = ____	10 – 1 = ____	6 – 1 = ____

Home Practice Minus Zero, Minus One Drills

Name: _____

Monday	Tuesday	Wednesday	Thursday	Friday
6 – 1 = ____	5 – 0 = ____	5 – 1 = ____	3 – 0 = ____	3 – 1 = ____
4 – 1 = ____	6 – 1 = ____	10 – 1 = ____	2 – 1 = ____	7 – 1 = ____
1 – 0 = ____	10 – 1 = ____	9 – 1 = ____	15 – 1 = ____	9 – 0 = ____
7 – 1 = ____	9 – 1 = ____	0 – 0 = ____	7 – 1 = ____	17 – 1 = ____
2 – 1 = ____	8 – 0 = ____	14 – 1 = ____	8 – 1 = ____	10 – 1 = ____
8 – 1 = ____	5 – 1 = ____	8 – 1 = ____	6 – 0 = ____	8 – 1 = ____
6 – 1 = ____	12 – 1 = ____	4 – 1 = ____	10 – 1 = ____	1 – 0 = ____
2 – 0 = ____	7 – 1 = ____	3 – 1 = ____	5 – 1 = ____	6 – 1 = ____
3 – 1 = ____	2 – 1 = ____	7 – 0 = ____	3 – 1 = ____	2 – 1 = ____
10 – 1 = ____	9 – 0 = ____	6 – 1 = ____	4 – 1 = ____	5 – 1 = ____
9 – 1 = ____	4 – 1 = ____	5 – 1 = ____	9 – 0 = ____	9 – 1 = ____
5 – 1 = ____	3 – 1 = ____	7 – 1 = ____	2 – 1 = ____	5 – 0 = ____
1 – 1 = ____	6 – 1 = ____	2 – 1 = ____	6 – 1 = ____	4 – 0 = ____
3 – 0 = ____	8 – 1 = ____	4 – 0 = ____	9 – 1 = ____	8 – 1 = ____
2 – 1 = ____	1 – 0 = ____	18 – 1 = ____	8 – 1 = ____	3 – 1 = ____
7 – 1 = ____	13 – 1 = ____	9 – 1 = ____	10 – 1 = ____	10 – 1 = ____
4 – 1 = ____	9 – 1 = ____	10 – 1 = ____	2 – 0 = ____	18 – 1 = ____
3 – 1 = ____	5 – 1 = ____	3 – 0 = ____	16 – 1 = ____	2 – 0 = ____
6 – 1 = ____	10 – 1 = ____	8 – 1 = ____	7 – 1 = ____	7 – 1 = ____
4 – 0 = ____	6 – 1 = ____	4 – 1 = ____	6 – 1 = ____	6 – 1 = ____
8 – 1 = ____	7 – 0 = ____	3 – 1 = ____	4 – 1 = ____	9 – 1 = ____
5 – 1 = ____	3 – 1 = ____	5 – 1 = ____	4 – 0 = ____	5 – 1 = ____
9 – 1 = ____	4 – 1 = ____	6 – 1 = ____	2 – 1 = ____	2 – 1 = ____
6 – 0 = ____	2 – 1 = ____	9 – 0 = ____	5 – 1 = ____	4 – 1 = ____
10 – 1 = ____	7 – 1 = ____	9 – 1 = ____	9 – 1 = ____	7 – 0 = ____
Score: ____/25 ____ Min. ____ Sec.	Score: ____/25 ____ Min. ____ Sec.	Score: ____/25 ____ Min. ____ Sec.	Score: ____/25 ____ Min. ____ Sec.	Score: ____/25 ____ Min. ____ Sec.

Minus Zero, Minus One Drill Sheet Test

Name: _____

6 − 1	10 − 1	9 − 1	5 − 0	12 − 1	7 − 1	2 − 1	4 − 1	3 − 1	6 − 0
8 − 1	13 − 1	9 − 0	5 − 1	10 − 1	6 − 1	3 − 1	4 − 1	2 − 1	7 − 0
5 − 1	10 − 1	9 − 1	14 − 1	8 − 1	9 − 1	6 − 1	5 − 0	2 − 1	4 − 1
7 − 1	3 − 0	8 − 1	12 − 1	10 − 1	5 − 0	9 − 1	6 − 1	7 − 0	4 − 1
2 − 1	8 − 0	13 − 1	3 − 1	10 − 1	9 − 1	2 − 0	8 − 1	6 − 0	3 − 1
4 − 0	7 − 1	2 − 1	8 − 0	6 − 1	3 − 1	10 − 1	9 − 1	5 − 1	1 − 1
2 − 0	7 − 1	4 − 1	3 − 0	8 − 1	5 − 1	6 − 1	9 − 0	10 − 1	11 − 1
4 − 1	2 − 1	7 − 0	8 − 1	3 − 0	9 − 1	8 − 1	10 − 1	16 − 1	7 − 1
6 − 0	4 − 1	2 − 1	5 − 1	9 − 0	3 − 1	7 − 1	17 − 1	10 − 1	8 − 0
6 − 0	2 − 1	5 − 1	9 − 1	4 − 0	8 − 1	3 − 1	10 − 1	18 − 1	7 − 0

Date: _____ Score: _____ /100 Time: _____ Min. _____ Sec.

OTM-1140 • SSK1-40 Timed Subtraction Facts

Minus Two Drills

Name: _____

Date: Monday _____ Score: _____ /25 Time: _____ Min. _____ Sec.

4 – 2 = ____	3 – 2 = ____	10 – 2 = ____	9 – 2 = ____	5 – 2 = ____
7 – 2 = ____	11 – 2 = ____	3 – 2 = ____	10 – 2 = ____	9 – 2 = ____
2 – 2 = ____	13 – 2 = ____	6 – 2 = ____	11 – 2 = ____	7 – 2 = ____
8 – 2 = ____	7 – 2 = ____	8 – 2 = ____	4 – 2 = ____	8 – 2 = ____
6 – 2 = ____	4 – 2 = ____	5 – 2 = ____	12 – 2 = ____	3 – 2 = ____

Date: Tuesday _____ Score: _____ /25 Time: _____ Min. _____ Sec.

6 – 2 = ____	10 – 2 = ____	9 – 2 = ____	5 – 2 = ____	11 – 2 = ____
7 – 2 = ____	6 – 2 = ____	5 – 2 = ____	4 – 2 = ____	10 – 2 = ____
14 – 2 = ____	8 – 2 = ____	10 – 2 = ____	15 – 2 = ____	9 – 2 = ____
4 – 2 = ____	11 – 2 = ____	6 – 2 = ____	7 – 2 = ____	11 – 2 = ____
3 – 2 = ____	9 – 2 = ____	3 – 2 = ____	5 – 2 = ____	8 – 2 = ____

Date: Wednesday _____ Score: _____ /25 Time: _____ Min. _____ Sec.

4 – 2 = ____	3 – 2 = ____	6 – 2 = ____	5 – 2 = ____	7 – 2 = ____
16 – 2 = ____	11 – 2 = ____	9 – 2 = ____	10 – 2 = ____	8 – 2 = ____
3 – 2 = ____	4 – 2 = ____	11 – 2 = ____	3 – 2 = ____	10 – 2 = ____
5 – 2 = ____	9 – 2 = ____	7 – 2 = ____	4 – 2 = ____	5 – 2 = ____
6 – 2 = ____	17 – 2 = ____	8 – 2 = ____	18 – 2 = ____	6 – 2 = ____

Date: Thursday _____ Score: _____ /25 Time: _____ Min. _____ Sec.

9 – 2 = ____	8 – 2 = ____	10 – 2 = ____	11 – 2 = ____	7 – 2 = ____
6 – 2 = ____	9 – 2 = ____	8 – 2 = ____	9 – 2 = ____	10 – 2 = ____
4 – 2 = ____	3 – 2 = ____	6 – 2 = ____	4 – 2 = ____	11 – 2 = ____
12 – 2 = ____	7 – 2 = ____	13 – 2 = ____	8 – 2 = ____	13 – 2 = ____
5 – 2 = ____	11 – 2 = ____	5 – 2 = ____	3 – 2 = ____	15 – 2 = ____

Date: Friday _____ Score: _____ /25 Time: _____ Min. _____ Sec.

6 – 2 = ____	9 – 2 = ____	5 – 2 = ____	14 – 2 = ____	4 – 2 = ____
7 – 2 = ____	10 – 2 = ____	7 – 2 = ____	11 – 2 = ____	16 – 2 = ____
3 – 2 = ____	5 – 2 = ____	4 – 2 = ____	3 – 2 = ____	8 – 2 = ____
8 – 2 = ____	9 – 2 = ____	15 – 2 = ____	10 – 2 = ____	6 – 2 = ____
11 – 2 = ____	6 – 2 = ____	8 – 2 = ____	9 – 2 = ____	3 – 2 = ____

Home Practice Minus Two Drills

Name: _____

Monday	Tuesday	Wednesday	Thursday	Friday
4 – 2 = ____	9 – 2 = ____	4 – 2 = ____	6 – 2 = ____	6 – 2 = ____
3 – 2 = ____	8 – 2 = ____	7 – 2 = ____	10 – 2 = ____	9 – 2 = ____
6 – 2 = ____	10 – 2 = ____	2 – 2 = ____	9 – 2 = ____	5 – 2 = ____
5 – 2 = ____	11 – 2 = ____	8 – 2 = ____	5 – 2 = ____	14 – 2 = ____
7 – 2 = ____	7 – 2 = ____	6 – 2 = ____	11 – 2 = ____	4 – 2 = ____
16 – 2 = ____	6 – 2 = ____	3 – 2 = ____	7 – 2 = ____	7 – 2 = ____
11 – 2 = ____	4 – 2 = ____	10 – 2 = ____	14 – 2 = ____	3 – 2 = ____
9 – 2 = ____	12 – 2 = ____	9 – 2 = ____	4 – 2 = ____	8 – 2 = ____
10 – 2 = ____	5 – 2 = ____	5 – 2 = ____	3 – 2 = ____	11 – 2 = ____
8 – 2 = ____	9 – 2 = ____	11 – 2 = ____	6 – 2 = ____	10 – 2 = ____
4 – 2 = ____	3 – 2 = ____	13 – 2 = ____	8 – 2 = ____	5 – 2 = ____
3 – 2 = ____	7 – 2 = ____	7 – 2 = ____	11 – 2 = ____	9 – 2 = ____
5 – 2 = ____	11 – 2 = ____	4 – 2 = ____	9 – 2 = ____	6 – 2 = ____
6 – 2 = ____	10 – 2 = ____	3 – 2 = ____	5 – 2 = ____	7 – 2 = ____
9 – 2 = ____	8 – 2 = ____	6 – 2 = ____	10 – 2 = ____	4 – 2 = ____
17 – 2 = ____	6 – 2 = ____	8 – 2 = ____	6 – 2 = ____	15 – 2 = ____
11 – 2 = ____	13 – 2 = ____	5 – 2 = ____	3 – 2 = ____	8 – 2 = ____
7 – 2 = ____	5 – 2 = ____	9 – 2 = ____	4 – 2 = ____	11 – 2 = ____
8 – 2 = ____	9 – 2 = ____	10 – 2 = ____	15 – 2 = ____	3 – 2 = ____
10 – 2 = ____	4 – 2 = ____	11 – 2 = ____	7 – 2 = ____	10 – 2 = ____
5 – 2 = ____	8 – 2 = ____	4 – 2 = ____	5 – 2 = ____	9 – 2 = ____
3 – 2 = ____	3 – 2 = ____	12 – 2 = ____	10 – 2 = ____	16 – 2 = ____
4 – 2 = ____	10 – 2 = ____	7 – 2 = ____	9 – 2 = ____	8 – 2 = ____
18 – 2 = ____	11 – 2 = ____	8 – 2 = ____	11 – 2 = ____	6 – 2 = ____
6 – 2 = ____	7 – 2 = ____	3 – 2 = ____	8 – 2 = ____	3 – 2 = ____
Score: ____ /25 _____ Min. _____ Sec.	Score: ____ /25 _____ Min. _____ Sec.	Score: ____ /25 _____ Min. _____ Sec.	Score: ____ /25 _____ Min. _____ Sec.	Score: ____ /25 _____ Min. _____ Sec.

Extra Practice Minus Two Drills

Name: _____

Day 1	Day 2	Day 3	Day 4	Day 5
___ − 2 = 2	___ − 2 = ___	4 − ___ = 2	9 − ___ = 7	6 − ___ = 4
7 − ___ = 5	10 − ___ = 8	___ − 2 = 1	8 − ___ = 6	9 − 2 = ___
2 − 2 = ___	9 − 2 = ___	6 − 2 = ___	10 − 2 = ___	___ − 2 = 3
___ − 2 = 6	___ − 2 = 3	5 − ___ = 3	11 − ___ = 9	14 − ___ = 12
6 − ___ = 4	11 − ___ = 9	___ − 2 = 5	7 − 2 = ___	4 − 2 = ___
3 − 2 = ___	7 − 2 = ___	16 − 2 = ___	___ − 2 = 4	___ − 2 = 5
___ − 2 = 8	___ − 2 = 12	11 − ___ = 9	4 − ___ = 2	3 − ___ = 1
9 − ___ = 7	4 − ___ = 2	___ − 2 = 7	12 − 2 = ___	___ − 2 = 6
5 − 2 = ___	3 − 2 = ___	10 − 2 = ___	5 − 3 = ___	11 − 2 = ___
___ − 2 = 9	___ − 2 = 4	8 − 2 = ___	___ − 2 = 7	10 − ___ = 8
13 − ___ = 7	8 − ___ = 6	___ − 2 = 2	3 − 2 = ___	5 − 2 = ___
7 − 2 = ___	11 − 2 = ___	3 − ___ = 1	7 − ___ = 5	9 − ___ = 7
___ − 2 = 2	___ − 2 = 7	5 − 2 = ___	11 − 2 = ___	___ − 2 = 4
3 − ___ = 1	5 − ___ = 13	___ − 2 = 4	___ − 2 = 8	7 − 2 = ___
6 − 2 = ___	10 − 2 = ___	9 − ___ = 7	8 − 2 = ___	4 − ___ = 2
___ − 2 = 6	___ − 2 = 4	17 − 2 = ___	___ − 2 = 4	15 − 2 = ___
5 − ___ = 3	3 − ___ = 1	___ − 2 = 9	13 − 2 = ___	8 − ___ = 6
9 − 2 = ___	4 − 2 = ___	7 − ___ = 5	5 − ___ = 3	___ − 2 = 9
___ − 2 = 8	___ − 2 = 13	8 − 2 = ___	9 − 2 = ___	3 − 2 = ___
11 − ___ = 9	7 − ___ = 5	10 − ___ = 8	___ − 2 = 2	10 − ___ = 8
___ − 2 = 2	5 − 2 = ___	___ − 2 = 3	___ − 2 = 6	___ − 2 = 7
12 − ___ = 10	___ − 2 = 8	3 − ___ = 1	3 − 2 = ___	16 − 2 = ___
7 − 2 = ___	9 − ___ = 7	4 − 2 = ___	10 − ___ = 8	___ − 2 = 6
___ − 2 = 6	11 − 2 = ___	18 − ___ = 16	___ − 2 = 9	6 − 2 = ___
3 − ___ = 1	___ − 2 = 6	___ − 2 = 4	7 − 2 = ___	___ − 2 = 1
Score: _____/25	Score: _____/25	Score: _____/25	Score: _____/25	Score: _____/25
_____ Min.	_____ Min.	_____ Min.	_____ Min.	_____ Min.
_____ Sec.	_____ Sec.	_____ Sec.	_____ Sec.	_____ Sec.

Minus Two Drill Sheet Test

Name: _____

4 − 2	7 − 2	2 − 2	8 − 2	6 − 2	3 − 2	10 − 2	9 − 2	5 − 2	11 − 2
13 − 2	7 − 2	4 − 2	3 − 2	6 − 2	8 − 2	5 − 2	9 − 2	10 − 2	4 − 2
11 − 2	8 − 2	12 − 2	10 − 2	7 − 2	9 − 2	3 − 2	5 − 2	6 − 2	11 − 2
7 − 2	14 − 2	4 − 2	3 − 2	6 − 2	8 − 2	11 − 2	9 − 2	5 − 2	10 − 2
6 − 2	3 − 2	15 − 2	7 − 2	4 − 2	5 − 2	10 − 2	8 − 2	11 − 2	9 − 2
4 − 2	5 − 2	6 − 2	3 − 2	16 − 2	7 − 2	11 − 2	9 − 2	10 − 2	8 − 2
3 − 2	17 − 2	4 − 2	11 − 2	5 − 2	10 − 2	6 − 2	7 − 2	8 − 2	9 − 2
5 − 2	3 − 2	18 − 2	9 − 2	4 − 2	8 − 2	10 − 2	4 − 2	11 − 2	6 − 2
12 − 2	7 − 2	11 − 2	5 − 2	6 − 2	10 − 2	9 − 2	8 − 2	3 − 2	7 − 2
6 − 2	13 − 2	5 − 2	9 − 2	4 − 2	8 − 2	3 − 2	10 − 2	7 − 2	11 − 2

Date: _____ **Score:** _____ /100 **Time:** _____ Min. _____ Sec.

OTM-1140 • SSK1-40 Timed Subtraction Facts

Minus Three Drills

Name: _____

Date: Monday _____ **Score:** _____ /25 **Time:** _____ **Min.** _____ **Sec.**

4 – 3 = ____	6 – 3 = ____	12 – 3 = ____	8 – 3 = ____	4 – 3 = ____
7 – 3 = ____	10 – 3 = ____	7 – 3 = ____	5 – 3 = ____	12 – 3 = ____
12 – 3 = ____	9 – 3 = ____	4 – 3 = ____	9 – 3 = ____	7 – 3 = ____
8 – 3 = ____	5 – 3 = ____	13 – 3 = ____	10 – 3 = ____	8 – 3 = ____
6 – 3 = ____	11 – 3 = ____	6 – 3 = ____	11 – 3 = ____	14 – 3 = ____

Date: Tuesday _____ **Score:** _____ /25 **Time:** _____ **Min.** _____ **Sec.**

6 – 3 = ____	7 – 3 = ____	8 – 3 = ____	6 – 3 = ____	5 – 3 = ____
10 – 3 = ____	12 – 3 = ____	11 – 3 = ____	16 – 3 = ____	10 – 3 = ____
9 – 3 = ____	4 – 3 = ____	9 – 3 = ____	4 – 3 = ____	9 – 3 = ____
5 – 3 = ____	15 – 3 = ____	5 – 3 = ____	12 – 3 = ____	11 – 3 = ____
11 – 3 = ____	6 – 3 = ____	10 – 3 = ____	7 – 3 = ____	8 – 3 = ____

Date: Wednesday _____ **Score:** _____ /25 **Time:** _____ **Min.** _____ **Sec.**

4 – 3 = ____	12 – 3 = ____	4 – 3 = ____	12 – 3 = ____	5 – 3 = ____
17 – 3 = ____	11 – 3 = ____	18 – 3 = ____	11 – 3 = ____	13 – 3 = ____
6 – 3 = ____	9 – 3 = ____	5 – 3 = ____	7 – 3 = ____	4 – 3 = ____
5 – 3 = ____	10 – 3 = ____	6 – 3 = ____	8 – 3 = ____	12 – 3 = ____
7 – 3 = ____	8 – 3 = ____	9 – 3 = ____	10 – 3 = ____	6 – 3 = ____

Date: Thursday _____ **Score:** _____ /25 **Time:** _____ **Min.** _____ **Sec.**

9 – 3 = ____	6 – 3 = ____	14 – 3 = ____	6 – 3 = ____	8 – 3 = ____
8 – 3 = ____	4 – 3 = ____	7 – 3 = ____	12 – 3 = ____	15 – 3 = ____
10 – 3 = ____	12 – 3 = ____	11 – 3 = ____	5 – 3 = ____	10 – 3 = ____
11 – 3 = ____	5 – 3 = ____	10 – 3 = ____	9 – 3 = ____	11 – 3 = ____
7 – 3 = ____	9 – 3 = ____	8 – 3 = ____	4 – 3 = ____	7 – 3 = ____

Date: Friday _____ **Score:** _____ /25 **Time:** _____ **Min.** _____ **Sec.**

6 – 3 = ____	7 – 3 = ____	5 – 3 = ____	12 – 3 = ____	9 – 3 = ____
9 – 3 = ____	16 – 3 = ____	9 – 3 = ____	8 – 3 = ____	12 – 3 = ____
5 – 3 = ____	8 – 3 = ____	6 – 3 = ____	11 – 3 = ____	8 – 3 = ____
12 – 3 = ____	11 – 3 = ____	7 – 3 = ____	17 – 3 = ____	6 – 3 = ____
4 – 3 = ____	10 – 3 = ____	4 – 3 = ____	10 – 3 = ____	18 – 3 = ____

Home Practice Minus Three Drills

Name: _____

Monday	Tuesday	Wednesday	Thursday	Friday
6 – 3 = ____	4 – 3 = ____	4 – 3 = ____	6 – 3 = ____	9 – 3 = ____
10 – 3 = ____	7 – 3 = ____	17 – 3 = ____	9 – 3 = ____	8 – 3 = ____
9 – 3 = ____	12 – 3 = ____	6 – 3 = ____	5 – 3 = ____	10 – 3 = ____
5 – 3 = ____	8 – 3 = ____	5 – 3 = ____	12 – 3 = ____	11 – 3 = ____
11 – 3 = ____	6 – 3 = ____	7 – 3 = ____	4 – 3 = ____	7 – 3 = ____
7 – 3 = ____	3 – 3 = ____	12 – 3 = ____	7 – 3 = ____	6 – 3 = ____
12 – 3 = ____	10 – 3 = ____	11 – 3 = ____	16 – 3 = ____	4 – 3 = ____
4 – 3 = ____	9 – 3 = ____	9 – 3 = ____	8 – 3 = ____	12 – 3 = ____
15 – 3 = ____	5 – 3 = ____	10 – 3 = ____	11 – 3 = ____	5 – 3 = ____
6 – 3 = ____	11 – 3 = ____	8 – 3 = ____	10 – 3 = ____	9 – 3 = ____
8 – 3 = ____	12 – 3 = ____	4 – 3 = ____	5 – 3 = ____	14 – 3 = ____
11 – 3 = ____	7 – 3 = ____	18 – 3 = ____	9 – 3 = ____	7 – 3 = ____
9 – 3 = ____	4 – 3 = ____	5 – 3 = ____	6 – 3 = ____	11 – 3 = ____
5 – 3 = ____	13 – 3 = ____	6 – 3 = ____	7 – 3 = ____	10 – 3 = ____
10 – 3 = ____	6 – 3 = ____	9 – 3 = ____	4 – 3 = ____	8 – 3 = ____
6 – 3 = ____	8 – 3 = ____	12 – 3 = ____	12 – 3 = ____	6 – 3 = ____
16 – 3 = ____	5 – 3 = ____	11 – 3 = ____	8 – 3 = ____	12 – 3 = ____
4 – 3 = ____	9 – 3 = ____	7 – 3 = ____	11 – 3 = ____	5 – 3 = ____
12 – 3 = ____	10 – 3 = ____	8 – 3 = ____	17 – 3 = ____	9 – 3 = ____
7 – 3 = ____	11 – 3 = ____	10 – 3 = ____	10 – 3 = ____	4 – 3 = ____
5 – 3 = ____	4 – 3 = ____	5 – 3 = ____	9 – 3 = ____	8 – 3 = ____
10 – 3 = ____	12 – 3 = ____	13 – 3 = ____	12 – 3 = ____	15 – 3 = ____
9 – 3 = ____	7 – 3 = ____	4 – 3 = ____	8 – 3 = ____	10 – 3 = ____
11 – 3 = ____	8 – 3 = ____	12 – 3 = ____	6 – 3 = ____	11 – 3 = ____
8 – 3 = ____	14 – 3 = ____	6 – 3 = ____	18 – 3 = ____	7 – 3 = ____
Score: ____/25	Score: ____/25	Score: ____/25	Score: ____/25	Score: ____/25
____ Min.	____ Min.	____ Min.	____ Min.	____ Min.
____ Sec.	____ Sec.	____ Sec.	____ Sec.	____ Sec.

Extra Practice Minus Three Drills

Name: _____

Day 1	Day 2	Day 3	Day 4	Day 5
4 − 3 = ___	6 − 3 = ___	4 − 3 = ___	3 − 3 = ___	8 − 3 = ___
___ − 3 = 4	___ − 3 = 12	___ − 3 = 0	9 − ___ = 6	3 − ___ = 0
13 − ___ = 10	9 − ___ = 6	6 − ___ = 3	___ − 3 = 5	7 − 3 = ___
8 − 3 = ___	5 − 3 = ___	5 − 3 = ___	10 − 3 = ___	13 − ___ = 10
___ − 3 = 3	___ − 3 = 9	7 − ___ = 4	___ − 3 = 13	___ − 3 = 1
3 − ___ = 0	7 − ___ = 4	15 − 3 = ___	7 − ___ = 4	11 − ___ = 8
17 − 3 = ___	14 − 3 = ___	___ − 3 = 15	14 − 3 = ___	10 − 3 = ___
___ − 3 = 6	___ − 3 = 1	9 − 3 = ___	___ − 3 = 1	___ − 3 = 6
5 − ___ = 2	3 − ___ = 0	10 − ___ = 7	17 − ___ = 14	5 − 3 = ___
14 − 3 = ___	8 − 3 = ___	___ − 3 = 5	5 − 3 = ___	___ − 3 = 5
___ − 3 = 11	___ − 3 = 3	4 − ___ = 1	___ − 3 = 6	6 − ___ = 3
7 − ___ = 4	13 − ___ = 10	6 − 3 = ___	3 − ___ = 0	3 − 3 = ___
4 − 3 = ___	9 − 3 = ___	___ − 3 = 0	7 − 3 = ___	___ − 3 = 1
___ − 3 = 0	___ − 3 = 2	5 − ___ = 3	___ − 3 = 14	7 − ___ = 4
6 − ___ = 3	10 − ___ = 7	9 − 3 = ___	10 − ___ = 7	12 − 3 = ___
8 − 3 = ___	8 − 3 = ___	___ − 3 = 9	8 − 3 = ___	14 − ___ = 11
___ − 3 = 2	___ − 3 = 3	15 − ___ = 12	___ − 3 = 3	5 − 3 = ___
9 − ___ = 6	3 − ___ = 0	7 − 3 = ___	18 − ___ = 15	9 − 3 = ___
10 − 3 = ___	16 − 3 = ___	___ − 3 = 7	13 − 3 = ___	___ − 3 = 14
___ − 3 = 8	___ − 3 = 9	8 − ___ = 5	3 − ___ = 3	3 − ___ = 0
4 − ___ = 1	7 − ___ = 4	5 − 3 = ___	___ − 3 = 15	___ − 3 = 3
13 − 3 = ___	5 − 3 = ___	___ − 3 = 13	4 − 3 = ___	8 − 3 = ___
___ − 3 = 4	___ − 3 = 7	7 − ___ = 4	___ − 3 = 4	13 − ___ = 10
8 − ___ = 5	9 − ___ = 6	8 − 3 = ___	11 − ___ = 8	7 − 3 = ___
3 − 3 = ___	14 − 3 = ___	3 − ___ = 0	9 − 3 = ___	___ − 3 = 1
Score: ____/25	Score: ____/25	Score: ____/25	Score: ____/25	Score: ____/25
____ Min.	____ Min.	____ Min.	____ Min.	____ Min.
____ Sec.	____ Sec.	____ Sec.	____ Sec.	____ Sec.

OTM-1140 • SSK1-40 Timed Subtraction Facts

Minus Three Drill Sheet Test

Name: _____

4 − 3	7 − 3	13 − 3	8 − 3	6 − 3	3 − 3	17 − 3	9 − 3	5 − 3	14 − 3
12 − 3	4 − 3	7 − 3	3 − 3	9 − 3	10 − 3	6 − 3	11 − 3	8 − 3	5 − 3
9 − 3	10 − 3	11 − 3	4 − 3	13 − 3	7 − 3	8 − 3	3 − 3	6 − 3	15 − 3
5 − 3	7 − 3	8 − 3	9 − 3	3 − 3	12 − 3	6 − 3	14 − 3	13 − 3	4 − 3
9 − 3	10 − 3	5 − 3	16 − 3	7 − 3	8 − 3	5 − 3	12 − 3	6 − 3	3 − 3
4 − 3	7 − 3	3 − 3	15 − 3	10 − 3	6 − 3	18 − 3	9 − 3	5 − 3	14 − 3
9 − 3	8 − 3	10 − 3	4 − 3	6 − 3	3 − 3	5 − 3	12 − 3	15 − 3	9 − 3
7 − 3	5 − 3	7 − 3	16 − 3	3 − 3	10 − 3	3 − 3	8 − 3	9 − 3	8 − 3
3 − 3	7 − 3	17 − 3	10 − 3	8 − 3	6 − 3	18 − 3	13 − 3	3 − 3	18 − 3
4 − 3	7 − 3	11 − 3	9 − 3	4 − 3	12 − 3	10 − 3	16 − 3	9 − 3	7 − 3

Date: _____   Score: _____ /100   Time: _____ Min. _____ Sec.

OTM-1140 • SSK1-40 Timed Subtraction Facts

Minus Four Drills

Name: _____

Date: Monday _____ Score: _____ /25 Time: _____ Min. _____ Sec.

4 – 4 = ____	13 – 4 = ____	12 – 4 = ____	8 – 4 = ____	15 – 4 = ____
7 – 4 = ____	10 – 4 = ____	7 – 4 = ____	5 – 4 = ____	12 – 4 = ____
12 – 4 = ____	9 – 4 = ____	14 – 4 = ____	9 – 4 = ____	7 – 4 = ____
8 – 4 = ____	5 – 4 = ____	13 – 4 = ____	10 – 4 = ____	8 – 4 = ____
6 – 4 = ____	11 – 4 = ____	6 – 4 = ____	11 – 4 = ____	13 – 4 = ____

Date: Tuesday _____ Score: _____ /25 Time: _____ Min. _____ Sec.

6 – 4 = ____	10 – 4 = ____	9 – 4 = ____	5 – 4 = ____	11 – 4 = ____
7 – 4 = ____	6 – 4 = ____	5 – 4 = ____	17 – 4 = ____	10 – 4 = ____
12 – 4 = ____	8 – 4 = ____	10 – 4 = ____	12 – 4 = ____	9 – 4 = ____
16 – 4 = ____	11 – 4 = ____	6 – 4 = ____	7 – 4 = ____	11 – 4 = ____
13 – 4 = ____	9 – 4 = ____	13 – 4 = ____	5 – 4 = ____	8 – 4 = ____

Date: Wednesday _____ Score: _____ /25 Time: _____ Min. _____ Sec.

18 – 4 = ____	13 – 4 = ____	6 – 4 = ____	5 – 4 = ____	7 – 4 = ____
12 – 4 = ____	11 – 4 = ____	9 – 4 = ____	10 – 4 = ____	8 – 4 = ____
4 – 4 = ____	6 – 4 = ____	11 – 4 = ____	13 – 4 = ____	6 – 4 = ____
13 – 4 = ____	9 – 4 = ____	7 – 4 = ____	14 – 4 = ____	9 – 4 = ____
5 – 4 = ____	12 – 4 = ____	8 – 4 = ____	12 – 4 = ____	8 – 4 = ____

Date: Thursday _____ Score: _____ /25 Time: _____ Min. _____ Sec.

10 – 4 = ____	12 – 4 = ____	11 – 4 = ____	5 – 4 = ____	10 – 4 = ____
11 – 4 = ____	5 – 4 = ____	10 – 4 = ____	9 – 4 = ____	11 – 4 = ____
7 – 4 = ____	9 – 4 = ____	8 – 4 = ____	16 – 4 = ____	7 – 4 = ____
6 – 4 = ____	13 – 4 = ____	6 – 4 = ____	8 – 4 = ____	6 – 4 = ____
15 – 4 = ____	7 – 4 = ____	12 – 4 = ____	15 – 4 = ____	9 – 4 = ____

Date: Friday _____ Score: _____ /25 Time: _____ Min. _____ Sec.

5 – 4 = ____	8 – 4 = ____	6 – 4 = ____	11 – 4 = ____	8 – 4 = ____
12 – 4 = ____	11 – 4 = ____	7 – 4 = ____	13 – 4 = ____	6 – 4 = ____
17 – 4 = ____	10 – 4 = ____	18 – 4 = ____	10 – 4 = ____	13 – 4 = ____
7 – 4 = ____	5 – 4 = ____	12 – 4 = ____	9 – 4 = ____	10 – 4 = ____
13 – 4 = ____	9 – 4 = ____	8 – 4 = ____	12 – 4 = ____	7 – 4 = ____

Home Practice Minus Four Drills

Name: _____

Monday	Tuesday	Wednesday	Thursday	Friday
4 – 4 = ____	6 – 4 = ____	9 – 4 = ____	18 – 4 = ____	6 – 4 = ____
7 – 4 = ____	9 – 4 = ____	8 – 4 = ____	13 – 4 = ____	10 – 4 = ____
12 – 4 = ____	5 – 4 = ____	10 – 4 = ____	6 – 4 = ____	9 – 4 = ____
8 – 4 = ____	12 – 4 = ____	11 – 4 = ____	5 – 4 = ____	5 – 4 = ____
6 – 4 = ____	17 – 4 = ____	7 – 4 = ____	7 – 4 = ____	11 – 4 = ____
13 – 4 = ____	7 – 4 = ____	6 – 4 = ____	12 – 4 = ____	7 – 4 = ____
10 – 4 = ____	13 – 4 = ____	15 – 4 = ____	11 – 4 = ____	12 – 4 = ____
9 – 4 = ____	8 – 4 = ____	12 – 4 = ____	9 – 4 = ____	16 – 4 = ____
5 – 4 = ____	11 – 4 = ____	5 – 4 = ____	10 – 4 = ____	13 – 4 = ____
11 – 4 = ____	10 – 4 = ____	9 – 4 = ____	8 – 4 = ____	6 – 4 = ____
12 – 4 = ____	5 – 4 = ____	13 – 4 = ____	4 – 4 = ____	8 – 4 = ____
7 – 4 = ____	9 – 4 = ____	7 – 4 = ____	13 – 4 = ____	11 – 4 = ____
14 – 4 = ____	6 – 4 = ____	11 – 4 = ____	5 – 4 = ____	9 – 4 = ____
13 – 4 = ____	7 – 4 = ____	10 – 4 = ____	6 – 4 = ____	5 – 4 = ____
6 – 4 = ____	18 – 4 = ____	8 – 4 = ____	9 – 4 = ____	10 – 4 = ____
8 – 4 = ____	12 – 4 = ____	6 – 4 = ____	12 – 4 = ____	6 – 4 = ____
5 – 4 = ____	8 – 4 = ____	12 – 4 = ____	11 – 4 = ____	13 – 4 = ____
9 – 4 = ____	11 – 4 = ____	5 – 4 = ____	7 – 4 = ____	17 – 4 = ____
10 – 4 = ____	13 – 4 = ____	9 – 4 = ____	8 – 4 = ____	12 – 4 = ____
11 – 4 = ____	10 – 4 = ____	16 – 4 = ____	10 – 4 = ____	7 – 4 = ____
15 – 4 = ____	9 – 4 = ____	8 – 4 = ____	5 – 4 = ____	5 – 4 = ____
12 – 4 = ____	12 – 4 = ____	15 – 4 = ____	13 – 4 = ____	10 – 4 = ____
7 – 4 = ____	8 – 4 = ____	10 – 4 = ____	14 – 4 = ____	9 – 4 = ____
8 – 4 = ____	6 – 4 = ____	11 – 4 = ____	12 – 4 = ____	11 – 4 = ____
13 – 4 = ____	13 – 4 = ____	7 – 4 = ____	6 – 4 = ____	8 – 4 = ____
Score: ____/25 _____ Min. _____ Sec.	Score: ____/25 _____ Min. _____ Sec.	Score: ____/25 _____ Min. _____ Sec.	Score: ____/25 _____ Min. _____ Sec.	Score: ____/25 _____ Min. _____ Sec.

Extra Practice Minus Four Drills

Name: _____

Day 1	Day 2	Day 3	Day 4	Day 5
4 - 4 = ___	6 - 4 = ___	18 - 4 = ___	9 - 4 = ___	___ - 4 = 2
___ - 4 = 3	___ - 4 = 6	13 - ___ = 9	___ - 4 = 4	9 - 4 = ___
12 - ___ = 8	9 - ___ = 5	6 - 4 = ___	10 - ___ = 6	5 - ___ = 1
8 - 4 = ___	5 - 4 = ___	___ - 4 = 1	11 - 4 = ___	___ - 4 = 8
___ - 4 = 2	___ - 4 = 7	___ - 4 = 3	___ - 4 = 3	17 - 4 = ___
13 - ___ = 9	7 - ___ = 3	12 - 4 = ___	6 - ___ = 2	___ - 4 = 3
10 - ___ = 6	12 - 4 = ___	11 - ___ = 7	15 - 4 = ___	13 - 4 = ___
9 - 4 = ___	16 - ___ = 12	___ - 4 = 5	___ - 4 = 8	___ - 4 = 4
5 - ___ = 1	___ - 4 = 7	10 - 4 = ___	5 - ___ = 1	11 - ___ = 7
___ - 4 = 7	6 - 4 = ___	___ - 4 = 4	9 - 4 = ___	10 - 4 = ___
12 - 4 = ___	8 - 4 = ___	4 - ___ = 0	___ - 4 = 9	___ - 4 = 1
___ - 4 = 3	___ - 4 = 7	13 - 4 = ___	7 - ___ = 3	9 - ___ = 5
14 - ___ = 10	9 - ___ = 5	___ - 4 = 1	11 - 4 = ___	6 - 4 = ___
13 - 4 = ___	5 - ___ = 1	6 - ___ = 2	10 - ___ = 6	___ - 4 = 3
___ - 4 = 2	___ - 4 = 6	9 - 4 = ___	___ - 4 = 4	18 - ___ = 14
8 - ___ = 4	6 - 4 = ___	___ - 4 = 8	6 - 4 = ___	12 - 4 = ___
5 - 4 = ___	___ - 4 = 9	11 - ___ = 7	12 - ___ = 8	___ - 4 = 4
___ - 4 = 5	17 - ___ = 13	7 - 4 = ___	___ - 4 = 1	11 - ___ = 7
10 - ___ = 6	12 - 4 = ___	___ - 4 = 4	9 - 4 = ___	13 - 4 = ___
11 - ___ = 7	7 - 4 = ___	10 - ___ = 6	___ - 4 = 12	___ - 4 = 6
15 - ___ = 11	___ - 4 = 1	5 - 4 = ___	8 - ___ = 4	9 - ___ = 5
___ - 4 = 8	10 - ___ = 6	___ - 4 = 9	15 - 4 = ___	12 - 4 = ___
7 - 4 = ___	9 - 4 = ___	14 - ___ = 6	___ - 4 = 6	___ - 4 = 4
___ - 4 = 4	11 - ___ = 7	12 - 4 = ___	11 - ___ = 7	6 - ___ = 2
13 - ___ = 9	8 - 4 = ___	___ - 4 = 2	7 - 4 = ___	___ - 4 = 9
Score: _____ /25	Score: _____ /25	Score: _____ /25	Score: _____ /25	Score: _____ /25
_____ Min.	_____ Min.	_____ Min.	_____ Min.	_____ Min.
_____ Sec.	_____ Sec.	_____ Sec.	_____ Sec.	_____ Sec.

Minus Four Drill Sheet Test

Name: _____

4 −4	7 −4	12 −4	8 −4	6 −4	13 −4	10 −4	9 −4	5 −4	11 −4
12 −4	7 −4	14 −4	13 −4	6 −4	8 −4	5 −4	9 −4	10 −4	15 −4
8 −4	13 −4	12 −4	6 −4	10 −4	7 −4	11 −4	5 −4	11 −4	9 −4
7 −4	16 −4	6 −4	13 −4	8 −4	9 −4	12 −4	10 −4	6 −4	11 −4
13 −4	17 −4	12 −4	7 −4	5 −4	10 −4	9 −4	5 −4	11 −4	8 −4
18 −4	13 −4	6 −4	12 −4	11 −4	8 −4	7 −4	4 −4	13 −4	5 −4
5 −4	9 −4	11 −4	7 −4	10 −4	9 −4	5 −4	14 −4	10 −4	8 −4
13 −4	12 −4	9 −4	6 −4	8 −4	15 −4	12 −4	5 −4	7 −4	11 −4
9 −4	7 −4	13 −4	11 −4	10 −4	5 −4	6 −4	12 −4	10 −4	8 −4
16 −4	12 −4	15 −4	6 −4	8 −4	10 −4	9 −4	11 −4	7 −4	18 −4

Date: _____   Score: _____ /100   Time: _____ Min. _____ Sec.

OTM-1140 • SSK1-40 Timed Subtraction Facts

Minus Five Drills

Name: _____

Date: Monday _____ Score: _____/25 Time: _____ Min. _____ Sec.

14 – 5 = ____	6 – 5 = ____	14 – 5 = ____	9 – 5 = ____	6 – 5 = ____
7 – 5 = ____	10 – 5 = ____	13 – 5 = ____	8 – 5 = ____	9 – 5 = ____
12 – 5 = ____	9 – 5 = ____	6 – 5 = ____	10 – 5 = ____	5 – 5 = ____
8 – 5 = ____	16 – 5 = ____	5 – 5 = ____	11 – 5 = ____	12 – 5 = ____
6 – 5 = ____	11 – 5 = ____	7 – 5 = ____	7 – 5 = ____	14 – 5 = ____

Date: Tuesday _____ Score: _____/25 Time: _____ Min. _____ Sec.

13 – 5 = ____	12 – 5 = ____	6 – 5 = ____	7 – 5 = ____	10 – 5 = ____
7 – 5 = ____	13 – 5 = ____	12 – 5 = ____	10 – 5 = ____	8 – 5 = ____
12 – 5 = ____	9 – 5 = ____	8 – 5 = ____	17 – 5 = ____	9 – 5 = ____
11 – 5 = ____	14 – 5 = ____	5 – 5 = ____	11 – 5 = ____	10 – 5 = ____
14 – 5 = ____	9 – 5 = ____	13 – 5 = ____	6 – 5 = ____	12 – 5 = ____

Date: Wednesday _____ Score: _____/25 Time: _____ Min. _____ Sec.

8 – 5 = ____	14 – 5 = ____	13 – 5 = ____	15 – 5 = ____	7 – 5 = ____
11 – 5 = ____	9 – 5 = ____	17 – 5 = ____	14 – 5 = ____	13 – 5 = ____
13 – 5 = ____	15 – 5 = ____	6 – 5 = ____	6 – 5 = ____	8 – 5 = ____
7 – 5 = ____	11 – 5 = ____	10 – 5 = ____	10 – 5 = ____	14 – 5 = ____
9 – 5 = ____	6 – 5 = ____	7 – 5 = ____	9 – 5 = ____	6 – 5 = ____

Date: Thursday _____ Score: _____/25 Time: _____ Min. _____ Sec.

8 – 5 = ____	11 – 5 = ____	7 – 5 = ____	8 – 5 = ____	10 – 5 = ____
6 – 5 = ____	12 – 5 = ____	18 – 5 = ____	9 – 5 = ____	14 – 5 = ____
12 – 5 = ____	8 – 5 = ____	11 – 5 = ____	13 – 5 = ____	10 – 5 = ____
15 – 5 = ____	9 – 5 = ____	10 – 5 = ____	11 – 5 = ____	18 – 5 = ____
13 – 5 = ____	14 – 5 = ____	12 – 5 = ____	7 – 5 = ____	16 – 5 = ____

Date: Friday _____ Score: _____/25 Time: _____ Min. _____ Sec.

8 – 5 = ____	12 – 5 = ____	8 – 5 = ____	5 – 5 = ____	17 – 5 = ____
9 – 5 = ____	7 – 5 = ____	11 – 5 = ____	10 – 5 = ____	7 – 5 = ____
12 – 5 = ____	9 – 5 = ____	12 – 5 = ____	15 – 5 = ____	18 – 5 = ____
10 – 5 = ____	14 – 5 = ____	6 – 5 = ____	16 – 5 = ____	10 – 5 = ____
13 – 5 = ____	10 – 5 = ____	13 – 5 = ____	8 – 5 = ____	6 – 5 = ____

Home Practice Minus Five Drills

Name: _____

Monday	Tuesday	Wednesday	Thursday	Friday
6 – 5 = ____	9 – 5 = ____	14 – 5 = ____	6 – 5 = ____	14 – 5 = ____
10 – 5 = ____	8 – 5 = ____	7 – 5 = ____	9 – 5 = ____	13 – 5 = ____
9 – 5 = ____	10 – 5 = ____	12 – 5 = ____	5 – 5 = ____	6 – 5 = ____
16 – 5 = ____	11 – 5 = ____	8 – 5 = ____	12 – 5 = ____	5 – 5 = ____
11 – 5 = ____	7 – 5 = ____	6 – 5 = ____	14 – 5 = ____	7 – 5 = ____
7 – 5 = ____	6 – 5 = ____	13 – 5 = ____	7 – 5 = ____	12 – 5 = ____
12 – 5 = ____	14 – 5 = ____	10 – 5 = ____	13 – 5 = ____	11 – 5 = ____
14 – 5 = ____	12 – 5 = ____	9 – 5 = ____	8 – 5 = ____	9 – 5 = ____
13 – 5 = ____	17 – 5 = ____	5 – 5 = ____	11 – 5 = ____	10 – 5 = ____
6 – 5 = ____	9 – 5 = ____	11 – 5 = ____	10 – 5 = ____	8 – 5 = ____
8 – 5 = ____	13 – 5 = ____	12 – 5 = ____	15 – 5 = ____	14 – 5 = ____
11 – 5 = ____	7 – 5 = ____	7 – 5 = ____	9 – 5 = ____	13 – 5 = ____
9 – 5 = ____	11 – 5 = ____	14 – 5 = ____	6 – 5 = ____	15 – 5 = ____
17 – 5 = ____	10 – 5 = ____	13 – 5 = ____	7 – 5 = ____	6 – 5 = ____
10 – 5 = ____	8 – 5 = ____	6 – 5 = ____	14 – 5 = ____	9 – 5 = ____
6 – 5 = ____	6 – 5 = ____	8 – 5 = ____	12 – 5 = ____	12 – 5 = ____
13 – 5 = ____	12 – 5 = ____	15 – 5 = ____	8 – 5 = ____	11 – 5 = ____
14 – 5 = ____	18 – 5 = ____	9 – 5 = ____	11 – 5 = ____	7 – 5 = ____
12 – 5 = ____	9 – 5 = ____	10 – 5 = ____	13 – 5 = ____	8 – 5 = ____
7 – 5 = ____	14 – 5 = ____	11 – 5 = ____	10 – 5 = ____	10 – 5 = ____
18 – 5 = ____	8 – 5 = ____	14 – 5 = ____	9 – 5 = ____	16 – 5 = ____
10 – 5 = ____	13 – 5 = ____	12 – 5 = ____	12 – 5 = ____	13 – 5 = ____
9 – 5 = ____	10 – 5 = ____	7 – 5 = ____	8 – 5 = ____	14 – 5 = ____
11 – 5 = ____	11 – 5 = ____	8 – 5 = ____	6 – 5 = ____	12 – 5 = ____
8 – 5 = ____	7 – 5 = ____	13 – 5 = ____	13 – 5 = ____	6 – 5 = ____
Score: ____/25 ____ Min. ____ Sec.	Score: ____/25 ____ Min. ____ Sec.	Score: ____/25 ____ Min. ____ Sec.	Score: ____/25 ____ Min. ____ Sec.	Score: ____/25 ____ Min. ____ Sec.

Extra Practice Minus Five Drills

Name: _____

Day 1	Day 2	Day 3	Day 4	Day 5
14 − 5 = ___	6 − 5 = ___	9 − 5 = ___	14 − 5 = ___	13 − 5 = ___
8 − 5 = ___	___ − 5 = 7	___ − 5 = 3	___ − 5 = 8	___ − 5 = 1
12 − ___ = 7	9 − ___ = 4	10 − ___ = 5	___ − 5 = 1	8 − ___ = 3
8 − 5 = ___	16 − 5 = ___	11 − 5 = ___	5 − ___ = 0	12 − 5 = ___
___ − 5 = 1	___ − 5 = 6	7 − ___ = 2	7 − 5 = ___	___ − 5 = 4
13 − ___ = 8	7 − ___ = 2	___ − 5 = 1	___ − 5 = 7	10 − ___ = 5
10 − 5 = ___	12 − 5 = ___	14 − 5 = ___	11 − 5 = ___	13 − 5 = ___
___ − 5 = 4	___ − 5 = 9	12 − ___ = 7	___ − 5 = 4	___ − 5 = 6
5 − ___ = 0	13 − ___ = 8	___ − 5 = 12	10 − 5 = ___	8 − ___ = 3
11 − 5 = ___	6 − 5 = ___	9 − 5 = ___	8 − 5 = ___	12 − ___ = 7
___ − 5 = 7	___ − 5 = 3	13 − ___ = 8	___ − 5 = 9	___ − 5 = 9
7 − ___ = 2	11 − ___ = 6	10 − 5 = ___	13 − ___ = 8	7 − 5 = ___
14 − 5 = ___	9 − 5 = ___	11 − 5 = ___	15 − 5 = ___	___ − 5 = 1
___ − 5 = 8	17 − ___ = 12	___ − 5 = 5	___ − 5 = 1	9 − ___ = 4
6 − ___ = 1	___ − 5 = 5	8 − ___ = 3	9 − ___ = 4	15 − 5 = ___
8 − 5 = ___	6 − 5 = ___	6 − 5 = ___	12 − 5 = ___	10 − ___ = 5
___ − 5 = 10	___ − 5 = 8	___ − 5 = 7	___ − 5 = 6	___ − 5 = 6
9 − ___ = 4	14 − 5 = ___	18 − 5 = ___	7 − ___ = 2	8 − 5 = ___
10 − 5 = ___	12 − 5 = ___	___ − 5 = 4	8 − 5 = ___	13 − 5 = ___
___ − 5 = 6	7 − ___ = 2	14 − ___ = 8	___ − 5 = 5	___ − 5 = 2
14 − ___ = 8	___ − 5 = 13	8 − 5 = ___	16 − ___ = 11	14 − ___ = 9
12 − 5 = ___	10 − 5 = ___	13 − ___ = 8	13 − 5 = ___	___ − 5 = 7
___ − 5 = 2	9 − ___ = 4	___ − 5 = 5	___ − 5 = 9	5 − 5 = ___
8 − ___ = 3	___ − 5 = 6	11 − 5 = ___	12 − 5 = ___	___ − 5 = 4
13 − 5 = ___	8 − 5 = ___	___ − 5 = 2	6 − 5 = ___	6 − ___ = 1
Score: _____/25	Score: _____/25	Score: _____/25	Score: _____/25	Score: _____/25
_____ Min.	_____ Min.	_____ Min.	_____ Min.	_____ Min.
_____ Sec.	_____ Sec.	_____ Sec.	_____ Sec.	_____ Sec.

Minus Five Drill Sheet Test

Name: _____

14 − 5	7 − 5	12 − 5	8 − 5	6 − 5	13 − 5	10 − 5	9 − 5	5 − 5	11 − 5
12 − 5	14 − 5	6 − 5	7 − 5	13 − 5	8 − 5	15 − 5	10 − 5	11 − 5	9 − 5
14 − 5	12 − 5	8 − 5	10 − 5	9 − 5	16 − 5	11 − 5	7 − 5	12 − 5	14 − 5
13 − 5	8 − 5	7 − 5	6 − 5	13 − 5	11 − 5	9 − 5	17 − 5	10 − 5	6 − 5
14 − 5	9 − 5	13 − 5	12 − 5	10 − 5	7 − 5	18 − 5	11 − 5	8 − 5	14 − 5
13 − 5	5 − 5	12 − 5	6 − 5	9 − 5	14 − 5	7 − 5	10 − 5	9 − 5	11 − 5
12 − 5	11 − 5	8 − 5	7 − 5	13 − 5	8 − 5	15 − 5	6 − 5	10 − 5	16 − 5
13 − 5	9 − 5	12 − 5	8 − 5	10 − 5	6 − 5	11 − 5	7 − 5	6 − 5	14 − 5
12 − 5	17 − 5	14 − 5	9 − 5	13 − 5	7 − 5	10 − 5	8 − 5	12 − 5	18 − 5
11 − 5	10 − 5	13 − 5	6 − 5	14 − 5	5 − 5	11 − 5	9 − 5	10 − 5	7 − 5

Date: _____ Score: _____/100 Time: _____ Min. _____ Sec.

–1, –2, –3, –4, –5 Timed Drill Test

Name: _____

Row 1	Row 2	Row 3	Row 4
7 – 4 = _____	9 – 4 = _____	4 – 1 = _____	5 – 2 = _____
15 – 4 = _____	4 – 4 = _____	18 – 4 = _____	10 – 4 = _____
3 – 2 = _____	6 – 2 = _____	8 – 2 = _____	9 – 2 = _____
5 – 5 = _____	14 – 5 = _____	9 – 5 = _____	10 – 5 = _____
7 – 3 = _____	13 – 3 = _____	18 – 3 = _____	6 – 3 = _____
4 – 1 = _____	2 – 1 = _____	6 – 1 = _____	9 – 1 = _____
13 – 4 = _____	9 – 4 = _____	14 – 4 = _____	17 – 4 = _____
6 – 2 = _____	9 – 2 = _____	16 – 2 = _____	2 – 2 = _____
18 – 5 = _____	13 – 5 = _____	8 – 5 = _____	9 – 5 = _____
8 – 4 = _____	14 – 3 = _____	7 – 2 = _____	8 – 3 = _____
17 – 5 = _____	8 – 1 = _____	5 – 1 = _____	2 – 1 = _____
4 – 2 = _____	9 – 3 = _____	6 – 3 = _____	11 – 4 = _____
8 – 5 = _____	11 – 2 = _____	17 – 3 = _____	8 – 2 = _____
6 – 4 = _____	4 – 2 = _____	7 – 5 = _____	12 – 5 = _____
11 – 3 = _____	8 – 3 = _____	4 – 3 = _____	3 – 3 = _____
5 – 1 = _____	3 – 1 = _____	5 – 5 = _____	8 – 4 = _____
6 – 4 = _____	10 – 4 = _____	11 – 4 = _____	16 – 4 = _____
13 – 2 = _____	5 – 4 = _____	12 – 2 = _____	3 – 2 = _____
16 – 5 = _____	11 – 5 = _____	6 – 5 = _____	7 – 5 = _____
10 – 3 = _____	15 – 3 = _____	5 – 3 = _____	5 – 3 = _____
1 – 1 = _____	7 – 1 = _____	9 – 4 = _____	3 – 1 = _____
5 – 4 = _____	10 – 5 = _____	12 – 4 = _____	12 – 4 = _____
10 – 2 = _____	14 – 2 = _____	5 – 2 = _____	7 – 2 = _____
15 – 5 = _____	7 – 4 = _____	1 – 1 = _____	6 – 5 = _____
12 – 3 = _____	16 – 3 = _____	7 – 3 = _____	4 – 3 = _____

Date: _____   Score: _____/100   Time: _____ Min. _____ Sec.

−1, −2, −3, −4, −5 Timed Drill Test

Name: _____

5 −2	10 −4	9 −2	10 −5	6 −3	9 −1	17 −4	2 −2	9 −5	8 −3
2 −1	11 −4	8 −2	12 −5	3 −3	8 −4	16 −4	3 −2	7 −5	5 −3
3 −1	12 −4	7 −2	6 −5	4 −3	7 −4	15 −4	5 −5	7 −3	4 −1
13 −4	6 −2	18 −5	8 −4	3 −2	17 −5	4 −2	8 −5	6 −4	11 −3
5 −1	6 −4	13 −2	16 −5	10 −3	1 −1	5 −4	10 −2	15 −5	12 −3
9 −1	4 −4	6 −2	14 −5	13 −3	2 −1	9 −4	9 −2	13 −5	14 −3
8 −1	9 −3	11 −2	4 −2	8 −3	3 −1	10 −4	5 −4	11 −5	15 −3
7 −1	10 −5	14 −2	7 −4	16 −3	4 −1	18 −4	8 −2	9 −5	18 −3
6 −1	14 −4	16 −2	8 −5	7 −2	5 −1	6 −3	17 −3	7 −5	4 −3
5 −5	11 −4	12 −2	6 −5	5 −3	9 −4	12 −4	5 −2	1 −1	7 −3

Date: _____   Score: _____ /100   Time: _____ Min. _____ Sec.

Minus Six Drills

Name: _____

Date: Monday _____ Score: _____ /25 Time: _____ Min. _____ Sec.

14 – 6 = ____	13 – 6 = ____	12 – 6 = ____	8 – 6 = ____	14 – 6 = ____
7 – 6 = ____	10 – 6 = ____	7 – 6 = ____	15 – 6 = ____	12 – 6 = ____
12 – 6 = ____	9 – 6 = ____	14 – 6 = ____	9 – 6 = ____	7 – 6 = ____
8 – 6 = ____	15 – 6 = ____	13 – 6 = ____	10 – 6 = ____	8 – 6 = ____
6 – 6 = ____	11 – 6 = ____	16 – 6 = ____	11 – 6 = ____	13 – 6 = ____

Date: Tuesday _____ Score: _____ /25 Time: _____ Min. _____ Sec.

16 – 6 = ____	10 – 6 = ____	9 – 6 = ____	15 – 6 = ____	11 – 6 = ____
7 – 6 = ____	12 – 6 = ____	14 – 6 = ____	13 – 6 = ____	16 – 6 = ____
8 – 6 = ____	11 – 6 = ____	15 – 6 = ____	9 – 6 = ____	10 – 6 = ____
6 – 6 = ____	13 – 6 = ____	14 – 6 = ____	12 – 6 = ____	7 – 6 = ____
15 – 6 = ____	10 – 6 = ____	9 – 6 = ____	11 – 6 = ____	8 – 6 = ____

Date: Wednesday _____ Score: _____ /25 Time: _____ Min. _____ Sec.

14 – 6 = ____	13 – 6 = ____	16 – 6 = ____	15 – 6 = ____	7 – 6 = ____
12 – 6 = ____	11 – 6 = ____	9 – 6 = ____	10 – 6 = ____	8 – 6 = ____
14 – 6 = ____	13 – 6 = ____	15 – 6 = ____	17 – 6 = ____	9 – 6 = ____
12 – 6 = ____	11 – 6 = ____	7 – 6 = ____	8 – 6 = ____	10 – 6 = ____
15 – 6 = ____	13 – 6 = ____	14 – 6 = ____	12 – 6 = ____	18 – 6 = ____

Date: Thursday _____ Score: _____ /25 Time: _____ Min. _____ Sec.

9 – 6 = ____	8 – 6 = ____	10 – 6 = ____	11 – 6 = ____	7 – 6 = ____
6 – 6 = ____	14 – 6 = ____	12 – 6 = ____	15 – 6 = ____	9 – 6 = ____
13 – 6 = ____	7 – 6 = ____	11 – 6 = ____	10 – 6 = ____	8 – 6 = ____
16 – 6 = ____	15 – 6 = ____	14 – 6 = ____	13 – 6 = ____	11 – 6 = ____
12 – 6 = ____	9 – 6 = ____	8 – 6 = ____	10 – 6 = ____	7 – 6 = ____

Date: Friday _____ Score: _____ /25 Time: _____ Min. _____ Sec.

17 – 6 = ____	9 – 6 = ____	15 – 6 = ____	12 – 6 = ____	14 – 6 = ____
7 – 6 = ____	13 – 6 = ____	8 – 6 = ____	11 – 6 = ____	10 – 6 = ____
15 – 6 = ____	9 – 6 = ____	18 – 6 = ____	7 – 6 = ____	14 – 6 = ____
12 – 6 = ____	8 – 6 = ____	11 – 6 = ____	13 – 6 = ____	10 – 6 = ____
9 – 6 = ____	12 – 6 = ____	8 – 6 = ____	6 – 6 = ____	13 – 6 = ____

Home Practice Minus Six Drills

Name: _____

Monday	Tuesday	Wednesday	Thursday	Friday
17 – 6 = ____	14 – 6 = ____	14 – 6 = ____	16 – 6 = ____	9 – 6 = ____
9 – 6 = ____	7 – 6 = ____	13 – 6 = ____	10 – 6 = ____	8 – 6 = ____
15 – 6 = ____	12 – 6 = ____	16 – 6 = ____	9 – 6 = ____	10 – 6 = ____
12 – 6 = ____	8 – 6 = ____	15 – 6 = ____	15 – 6 = ____	11 – 6 = ____
14 – 6 = ____	6 – 6 = ____	7 – 6 = ____	11 – 6 = ____	7 – 6 = ____
7 – 6 = ____	13 – 6 = ____	12 – 6 = ____	7 – 6 = ____	6 – 6 = ____
13 – 6 = ____	10 – 6 = ____	11 – 6 = ____	12 – 6 = ____	14 – 6 = ____
8 – 6 = ____	9 – 6 = ____	9 – 6 = ____	14 – 6 = ____	12 – 6 = ____
11 – 6 = ____	15 – 6 = ____	10 – 6 = ____	13 – 6 = ____	15 – 6 = ____
10 – 6 = ____	11 – 6 = ____	8 – 6 = ____	16 – 6 = ____	9 – 6 = ____
15 – 6 = ____	12 – 6 = ____	14 – 6 = ____	8 – 6 = ____	13 – 6 = ____
9 – 6 = ____	7 – 6 = ____	13 – 6 = ____	11 – 6 = ____	7 – 6 = ____
18 – 6 = ____	14 – 6 = ____	15 – 6 = ____	9 – 6 = ____	11 – 6 = ____
7 – 6 = ____	13 – 6 = ____	17 – 6 = ____	15 – 6 = ____	10 – 6 = ____
14 – 6 = ____	16 – 6 = ____	9 – 6 = ____	10 – 6 = ____	8 – 6 = ____
12 – 6 = ____	8 – 6 = ____	12 – 6 = ____	6 – 6 = ____	16 – 6 = ____
8 – 6 = ____	15 – 6 = ____	11 – 6 = ____	13 – 6 = ____	12 – 6 = ____
11 – 6 = ____	9 – 6 = ____	7 – 6 = ____	14 – 6 = ____	15 – 6 = ____
13 – 6 = ____	10 – 6 = ____	8 – 6 = ____	12 – 6 = ____	9 – 6 = ____
10 – 6 = ____	11 – 6 = ____	10 – 6 = ____	7 – 6 = ____	14 – 6 = ____
9 – 6 = ____	14 – 6 = ____	15 – 6 = ____	15 – 6 = ____	8 – 6 = ____
12 – 6 = ____	12 – 6 = ____	13 – 6 = ____	10 – 6 = ____	13 – 6 = ____
8 – 6 = ____	7 – 6 = ____	14 – 6 = ____	9 – 6 = ____	10 – 6 = ____
6 – 6 = ____	8 – 6 = ____	12 – 6 = ____	11 – 6 = ____	11 – 6 = ____
13 – 6 = ____	13 – 6 = ____	18 – 6 = ____	8 – 6 = ____	7 – 6 = ____
Score: ____/25 ____ Min. ____ Sec.	Score: ____/25 ____ Min. ____ Sec.	Score: ____/25 ____ Min. ____ Sec.	Score: ____/25 ____ Min. ____ Sec.	Score: ____/25 ____ Min. ____ Sec.

Extra Practice Minus Six Drills

Name: _____

Day 1	Day 2	Day 3	Day 4	Day 5
14 - 6 = ___	___ - 6 = 10	14 - ___ = 8	9 - 6 = ___	___ - 6 = 11
___ - 6 = 1	10 - 6 = ___	13 - 6 = ___	___ - 6 = 2	9 - ___ = 3
12 - ___ = 6	___ - 6 = 3	___ - 6 = 10	10 - ___ = 4	15 - 6 = ___
8 - 6 = ___	15 - ___ = 9	15 - ___ = 9	11 - 6 = ___	___ - 6 = 6
___ - 6 = ___	11 - 6 = ___	___ - 6 = 1	___ - 6 = 1	14 - ___ = 8
13 - ___ = 6	___ - 6 = 1	12 - 6 = ___	6 - ___ = 0	7 - 6 = ___
10 - 6 = ___	___ - 6 = 6	11 - 6 = ___	14 - 6 = ___	___ - 6 = 7
___ - 6 = 3	14 - 6 = ___	9 - ___ = 3	___ - 6 = 6	8 - ___ = 2
15 - ___ = 7	13 - ___ = 7	___ - 6 = 4	15 - ___ = 9	11 - 6 = ___
11 - 6 = ___	16 - ___ = 10	8 - 6 = ___	9 - 6 = ___	___ - 6 = 4
___ - 6 = 6	8 - 6 = ___	14 - ___ = 8	___ - 6 = 7	15 - ___ = 9
7 - ___ = 1	11 - ___ = 5	13 - 6 = ___	7 - 6 = ___	9 - 6 = ___
14 - 6 = ___	9 - ___ = 3	___ - 6 = 9	11 - ___ = 5	___ - 6 = 12
___ - 6 = 7	15 - 6 = ___	17 - 6 = ___	10 - 6 = ___	7 - ___ = 1
16 - ___ = 10	___ - 6 = 4	9 - ___ = 3	8 - 6 = ___	14 - 6 = ___
8 - 6 = ___	6 - 6 = ___	___ - 6 = 6	___ - 6 = 10	___ - 6 = 6
___ - 6 = 9	___ - 6 = 7	11 - 6 = ___	12 - ___ = 6	8 - ___ = 2
9 - ___ = 3	14 - 6 = ___	7 - ___ = 1	15 - 6 = ___	11 - 6 = ___
10 - 6 = ___	12 - ___ = 6	8 - 6 = ___	9 - 6 = ___	13 - ___ = 7
11 - ___ = 5	___ - 6 = 1	10 - ___ = 4	___ - 6 = 8	___ - 6 = 4
14 - ___ = 8	15 - 6 = ___	15 - 6 = ___	8 - ___ = 2	9 - 6 = ___
12 - 6 = ___	10 - 6 = ___	13 - ___ = 7	13 - 6 = ___	___ - 6 = 6
___ - 6 = 1	___ - 6 = 3	___ - 6 = 8	10 - ___ = 4	8 - ___ = 2
8 - ___ = 2	11 - 6 = ___	12 - ___ = 6	___ - 6 = 5	6 - ___ = 0
13 - 6 = ___	___ - 6 = 2	___ - 6 = 12	7 - 6 = ___	13 - 6 = ___
Score: _____/25	Score: _____/25	Score: _____/25	Score: _____/25	Score: _____/25
_____ Min.	_____ Min.	_____ Min.	_____ Min.	_____ Min.
_____ Sec.	_____ Sec.	_____ Sec.	_____ Sec.	_____ Sec.

Minus Six Drill Sheet Test

Name: _____

14 − 6	7 − 6	12 − 6	8 − 6	6 − 6	13 − 6	10 − 6	9 − 6	15 − 6	11 − 6
12 − 6	7 − 6	14 − 6	13 − 6	16 − 6	8 − 6	15 − 6	10 − 6	11 − 6	9 − 6
14 − 6	12 − 6	7 − 6	8 − 6	13 − 6	16 − 6	10 − 6	9 − 6	15 − 6	11 − 6
7 − 6	13 − 6	16 − 6	12 − 6	8 − 6	11 − 6	14 − 6	15 − 6	10 − 6	13 − 6
6 − 6	14 − 6	15 − 6	10 − 6	13 − 6	9 − 6	12 − 6	8 − 6	7 − 6	9 − 6
11 − 6	10 − 6	12 − 6	9 − 6	15 − 6	18 − 6	8 − 6	13 − 6	10 − 6	14 − 6
7 − 6	14 − 6	11 − 6	13 − 6	7 − 6	6 − 6	9 − 6	12 − 6	11 − 6	15 − 6
10 − 6	8 − 6	16 − 6	12 − 6	15 − 6	14 − 6	8 − 6	13 − 6	10 − 6	9 − 6
11 − 6	7 − 6	17 − 6	9 − 6	15 − 6	12 − 6	14 − 6	7 − 6	13 − 6	8 − 6
10 − 6	15 − 6	18 − 6	14 − 6	11 − 6	7 − 6	8 − 6	11 − 6	9 − 6	12 − 6

Date: _____   Score: _____ /100   Time: _____ Min. _____ Sec.

OTM-1140 • SSK1-40 Timed Subtraction Facts

Minus Seven Drills

Name: _____

Date: Monday _____ Score: _____ /25 Time: _____ Min. _____ Sec.

14 – 7 = ____	13 – 7 = ____	12 – 7 = ____	8 – 7 = ____	14 – 7 = ____
7 – 7 = ____	10 – 7 = ____	7 – 7 = ____	15 – 7 = ____	12 – 7 = ____
12 – 7 = ____	9 – 7 = ____	14 – 7 = ____	9 – 7 = ____	7 – 7 = ____
8 – 7 = ____	15 – 7 = ____	13 – 7 = ____	10 – 7 = ____	8 – 7 = ____
6 – 7 = ____	11 – 7 = ____	16 – 7 = ____	11 – 7 = ____	13 – 7 = ____

Date: Tuesday _____ Score: _____ /25 Time: _____ Min. _____ Sec.

16 – 7 = ____	7 – 7 = ____	8 – 7 = ____	6 – 7 = ____	15 – 7 = ____
10 – 7 = ____	12 – 7 = ____	11 – 7 = ____	13 – 7 = ____	10 – 7 = ____
9 – 7 = ____	14 – 7 = ____	9 – 7 = ____	14 – 7 = ____	9 – 7 = ____
15 – 7 = ____	13 – 7 = ____	15 – 7 = ____	12 – 7 = ____	11 – 7 = ____
11 – 7 = ____	16 – 7 = ____	10 – 7 = ____	7 – 7 = ____	8 – 7 = ____

Date: Wednesday _____ Score: _____ /25 Time: _____ Min. _____ Sec.

14 – 7 = ____	12 – 7 = ____	14 – 7 = ____	12 – 7 = ____	15 – 7 = ____
13 – 7 = ____	11 – 7 = ____	13 – 7 = ____	11 – 7 = ____	13 – 7 = ____
16 – 7 = ____	9 – 7 = ____	15 – 7 = ____	7 – 7 = ____	14 – 7 = ____
15 – 7 = ____	10 – 7 = ____	17 – 7 = ____	8 – 7 = ____	12 – 7 = ____
7 – 7 = ____	8 – 7 = ____	9 – 7 = ____	10 – 7 = ____	18 – 7 = ____

Date: Thursday _____ Score: _____ /25 Time: _____ Min. _____ Sec.

9 – 7 = ____	6 – 7 = ____	13 – 7 = ____	16 – 7 = ____	8 – 7 = ____
8 – 7 = ____	14 – 7 = ____	7 – 7 = ____	12 – 7 = ____	13 – 7 = ____
10 – 7 = ____	12 – 7 = ____	11 – 7 = ____	15 – 7 = ____	10 – 7 = ____
11 – 7 = ____	15 – 7 = ____	10 – 7 = ____	9 – 7 = ____	11 – 7 = ____
7 – 7 = ____	9 – 7 = ____	8 – 7 = ____	14 – 7 = ____	7 – 7 = ____

Date: Friday _____ Score: _____ /25 Time: _____ Min. _____ Sec.

17 – 7 = ____	7 – 7 = ____	15 – 7 = ____	12 – 7 = ____	9 – 7 = ____
9 – 7 = ____	13 – 7 = ____	9 – 7 = ____	8 – 7 = ____	12 – 7 = ____
15 – 7 = ____	8 – 7 = ____	18 – 7 = ____	11 – 7 = ____	8 – 7 = ____
12 – 7 = ____	11 – 7 = ____	7 – 7 = ____	13 – 7 = ____	16 – 7 = ____
14 – 7 = ____	10 – 7 = ____	14 – 7 = ____	10 – 7 = ____	13 – 7 = ____

Home Practice Minus Seven Drills

Name: _____

Monday	Tuesday	Wednesday	Thursday	Friday
9 – 7 = ____	14 – 7 = ____	16 – 7 = ____	14 – 7 = ____	16 – 7 = ____
8 – 7 = ____	13 – 7 = ____	9 – 7 = ____	7 – 7 = ____	10 – 7 = ____
10 – 7 = ____	16 – 7 = ____	15 – 7 = ____	12 – 7 = ____	9 – 7 = ____
11 – 7 = ____	15 – 7 = ____	12 – 7 = ____	8 – 7 = ____	15 – 7 = ____
17 – 7 = ____	18 – 7 = ____	14 – 7 = ____	16 – 7 = ____	11 – 7 = ____
16 – 7 = ____	12 – 7 = ____	17 – 7 = ____	13 – 7 = ____	7 – 7 = ____
14 – 7 = ____	11 – 7 = ____	13 – 7 = ____	10 – 7 = ____	12 – 7 = ____
12 – 7 = ____	9 – 7 = ____	8 – 7 = ____	9 – 7 = ____	14 – 7 = ____
15 – 7 = ____	10 – 7 = ____	11 – 7 = ____	15 – 7 = ____	13 – 7 = ____
9 – 7 = ____	8 – 7 = ____	10 – 7 = ____	11 – 7 = ____	16 – 7 = ____
13 – 7 = ____	14 – 7 = ____	15 – 7 = ____	12 – 7 = ____	8 – 7 = ____
18 – 7 = ____	13 – 7 = ____	9 – 7 = ____	17 – 7 = ____	11 – 7 = ____
11 – 7 = ____	15 – 7 = ____	16 – 7 = ____	14 – 7 = ____	9 – 7 = ____
10 – 7 = ____	16 – 7 = ____	18 – 7 = ____	13 – 7 = ____	15 – 7 = ____
8 – 7 = ____	9 – 7 = ____	14 – 7 = ____	16 – 7 = ____	10 – 7 = ____
16 – 7 = ____	12 – 7 = ____	12 – 7 = ____	8 – 7 = ____	16 – 7 = ____
12 – 7 = ____	11 – 7 = ____	8 – 7 = ____	15 – 7 = ____	13 – 7 = ____
15 – 7 = ____	7 – 7 = ____	11 – 7 = ____	9 – 7 = ____	14 – 7 = ____
9 – 7 = ____	8 – 7 = ____	13 – 7 = ____	10 – 7 = ____	12 – 7 = ____
14 – 7 = ____	10 – 7 = ____	10 – 7 = ____	11 – 7 = ____	17 – 7 = ____
8 – 7 = ____	15 – 7 = ____	9 – 7 = ____	14 – 7 = ____	15 – 7 = ____
13 – 7 = ____	13 – 7 = ____	12 – 7 = ____	12 – 7 = ____	10 – 7 = ____
10 – 7 = ____	14 – 7 = ____	8 – 7 = ____	18 – 7 = ____	9 – 7 = ____
11 – 7 = ____	12 – 7 = ____	16 – 7 = ____	8 – 7 = ____	11 – 7 = ____
7 – 7 = ____	16 – 7 = ____	13 – 7 = ____	13 – 7 = ____	8 – 7 = ____
Score: ____ /25 ____ Min. ____ Sec.	Score: ____ /25 ____ Min. ____ Sec.	Score: ____ /25 ____ Min. ____ Sec.	Score: ____ /25 ____ Min. ____ Sec.	Score: ____ /25 ____ Min. ____ Sec.

Extra Practice Minus Seven Drills

Name: _____

Day 1	Day 2	Day 3	Day 4	Day 5
14 – 7 = ___	16 – ___ = 9	14 – ___ = 7	___ – 7 = 2	16 – ___ = 9
___ – 7 = 0	___ – 7 = 3	13 – 7 = ___	8 – ___ = 1	9 – 7 = ___
12 – ___ = 5	9 – 7 = ___	___ – 7 = 9	10 – 7 = ___	___ – 7 = 8
8 – 7 = ___	15 – ___ = 8	15 – ___ = 8	___ – 7 = 4	12 – ___ = 5
___ – 7 = 9	___ – 7 = 4	18 – 7 = ___	17 – ___ = 10	14 – 7 = ___
13 – ___ = 6	7 – 7 = ___	___ – 7 = 5	___ – 7 = 9	___ – 7 = 10
10 – 7 = ___	12 – ___ = 5	11 – ___ = 4	14 – ___ = 7	13 – 7 = ___
___ – 7 = 2	___ – 7 = 7	9 – 7 = ___	___ – 7 = 5	___ – 7 = 1
15 – ___ = 8	13 – 7 = ___	___ – 7 = 3	15 – ___ = 8	11 – ___ = 4
11 – 7 = ___	16 – ___ = 9	8 – ___ = 1	9 – 7 = ___	___ – 7 = 3
___ – 7 = 5	___ – 7 = 1	___ – 7 = 7	13 – ___ = 7	15 – ___ = 8
17 – ___ = 10	11 – 7 = ___	13 – 7 = ___	___ – 7 = 11	___ – 7 = 2
14 – ___ = 7	9 – ___ = 2	___ – 7 = 8	11 – 7 = ___	16 – 7 = ___
13 – 7 = ___	15 – 7 = ___	16 – ___ = 9	10 – 7 = ___	18 – ___ = 11
___ – 7 = 9	___ – 7 = 3	9 – 7 = ___	8 – ___ = 1	___ – 7 = 6
8 – ___ = 1	16 – 7 = ___	12 – ___ = 7	___ – 7 = 9	12 – ___ = 5
15 – 7 = ___	___ – 7 = 6	___ – 7 = 4	12 – ___ = 5	8 – 7 = ___
___ – 7 = 2	14 – ___ = 7	7 – ___ = 0	___ – 7 = 8	___ – 7 = 4
10 – 7 = ___	12 – 7 = ___	8 – 7 = ___	9 – ___ = 2	13 – ___ = 6
___ – 7 = 4	17 – ___ = 10	10 – ___ = 3	14 – 7 = ___	10 – 7 = ___
14 – ___ = 7	___ – 7 = 8	___ – 7 = 8	8 – 7 = ___	___ – 7 = 2
12 – 7 = ___	10 – 7 = ___	13 – 7 = ___	___ – 7 = 6	12 – ___ = 5
___ – 7 = 11	___ – 7 = 2	___ – 7 = 7	10 – ___ = 3	8 – 7 = ___
8 – ___ = 1	11 – ___ = 4	12 – ___ = 5	11 – 7 = ___	___ – 7 = 9
13 – 7 = ___	8 – 7 = ___	16 – 7 = ___	7 – ___ = 0	13 – ___ = 6
Score: _____/25	Score: _____/25	Score: _____/25	Score: _____/25	Score: _____/25
_____ Min.	_____ Min.	_____ Min.	_____ Min.	_____ Min.
_____ Sec.	_____ Sec.	_____ Sec.	_____ Sec.	_____ Sec.

Minus Seven Drill Sheet Test

Name: _____

14 − 7	7 − 7	12 − 7	8 − 7	16 − 7	13 − 7	10 − 7	9 − 7	15 − 7	11 − 7
12 − 7	17 − 7	14 − 7	13 − 7	16 − 7	8 − 7	15 − 7	9 − 7	10 − 7	14 − 7
18 − 7	8 − 7	11 − 7	16 − 7	14 − 7	10 − 7	12 − 7	15 − 7	13 − 7	9 − 7
11 − 7	7 − 7	12 − 7	14 − 7	13 − 7	16 − 7	8 − 7	11 − 7	9 − 7	15 − 7
10 − 7	16 − 7	13 − 7	12 − 7	15 − 7	14 − 7	10 − 7	17 − 7	11 − 7	9 − 7
8 − 7	14 − 7	18 − 7	15 − 7	11 − 7	13 − 7	9 − 7	10 − 7	12 − 7	16 − 7
13 − 7	12 − 7	9 − 7	8 − 7	7 − 7	15 − 7	14 − 7	16 − 7	8 − 7	11 − 7
10 − 7	15 − 7	13 − 7	14 − 7	12 − 7	16 − 7	9 − 7	10 − 7	11 − 7	17 − 7
16 − 7	14 − 7	12 − 7	8 − 7	15 − 7	9 − 7	18 − 7	13 − 7	10 − 7	8 − 7
12 − 7	9 − 7	10 − 7	11 − 7	14 − 7	16 − 7	8 − 7	15 − 7	7 − 7	13 − 7

Date: _____   **Score:** _____ /100   **Time:** _____ Min. _____ Sec.

OTM-1140 • SSK1-40 Timed Subtraction Facts

Minus Eight Drills

Name: _____

| Date: Monday _____ | | | Score: _____/25 | Time: _____ Min. _____ Sec. |

14 – 8 = _____   13 – 8 = _____   12 – 8 = _____   18 – 8 = _____   14 – 8 = _____
17 – 8 = _____   10 – 8 = _____   17 – 8 = _____   15 – 8 = _____   12 – 8 = _____
12 – 8 = _____   9 – 8 = _____   14 – 8 = _____   9 – 8 = _____   17 – 8 = _____
 8 – 8 = _____   15 – 8 = _____   13 – 8 = _____   10 – 8 = _____   8 – 8 = _____
16 – 8 = _____   11 – 8 = _____   16 – 8 = _____   11 – 8 = _____   13 – 8 = _____

| Date: Tuesday _____ | | | Score: _____/25 | Time: _____ Min. _____ Sec. |

16 – 8 = _____   17 – 8 = _____   18 – 8 = _____   16 – 8 = _____   15 – 8 = _____
10 – 8 = _____   12 – 8 = _____   11 – 8 = _____   13 – 8 = _____   10 – 8 = _____
 9 – 8 = _____   14 – 8 = _____   9 – 8 = _____   14 – 8 = _____   9 – 8 = _____
15 – 8 = _____   13 – 8 = _____   15 – 8 = _____   12 – 8 = _____   11 – 8 = _____
11 – 8 = _____   16 – 8 = _____   10 – 8 = _____   17 – 8 = _____   8 – 8 = _____

| Date: Wednesday _____ | | | Score: _____/25 | Time: _____ Min. _____ Sec. |

14 – 8 = _____   12 – 8 = _____   14 – 8 = _____   12 – 8 = _____   15 – 8 = _____
13 – 8 = _____   11 – 8 = _____   13 – 8 = _____   11 – 8 = _____   13 – 8 = _____
16 – 8 = _____   9 – 8 = _____   15 – 8 = _____   17 – 8 = _____   14 – 8 = _____
15 – 8 = _____   10 – 8 = _____   16 – 8 = _____   18 – 8 = _____   12 – 8 = _____
17 – 8 = _____   8 – 8 = _____   9 – 8 = _____   10 – 8 = _____   16 – 8 = _____

| Date: Thursday _____ | | | Score: _____/25 | Time: _____ Min. _____ Sec. |

 9 – 8 = _____   16 – 8 = _____   13 – 8 = _____   16 – 8 = _____   8 – 8 = _____
 8 – 8 = _____   14 – 8 = _____   17 – 8 = _____   12 – 8 = _____   13 – 8 = _____
10 – 8 = _____   12 – 8 = _____   11 – 8 = _____   15 – 8 = _____   10 – 8 = _____
11 – 8 = _____   15 – 8 = _____   10 – 8 = _____   9 – 8 = _____   11 – 8 = _____
17 – 8 = _____   9 – 8 = _____   18 – 8 = _____   14 – 8 = _____   17 – 8 = _____

| Date: Friday _____ | | | Score: _____/25 | Time: _____ Min. _____ Sec. |

16 – 8 = _____   17 – 8 = _____   15 – 8 = _____   12 – 8 = _____   9 – 8 = _____
 9 – 8 = _____   13 – 8 = _____   9 – 8 = _____   8 – 8 = _____   12 – 8 = _____
15 – 8 = _____   18 – 8 = _____   16 – 8 = _____   11 – 8 = _____   18 – 8 = _____
12 – 8 = _____   11 – 8 = _____   17 – 8 = _____   13 – 8 = _____   16 – 8 = _____
14 – 8 = _____   10 – 8 = _____   14 – 8 = _____   10 – 8 = _____   13 – 8 = _____

Home Practice Minus Eight Drills

Name: _____

Monday	Tuesday	Wednesday	Thursday	Friday
14 – 8 = ____	9 – 8 = ____	16 – 8 = ____	14 – 8 = ____	16 – 8 = ____
17 – 8 = ____	8 – 8 = ____	9 – 8 = ____	13 – 8 = ____	10 – 8 = ____
12 – 8 = ____	10 – 8 = ____	15 – 8 = ____	16 – 8 = ____	9 – 8 = ____
8 – 8 = ____	11 – 8 = ____	12 – 8 = ____	15 – 8 = ____	15 – 8 = ____
16 – 8 = ____	17 – 8 = ____	14 – 8 = ____	17 – 8 = ____	11 – 8 = ____
13 – 8 = ____	16 – 8 = ____	17 – 8 = ____	12 – 8 = ____	17 – 8 = ____
10 – 8 = ____	14 – 8 = ____	13 – 8 = ____	11 – 8 = ____	12 – 8 = ____
9 – 8 = ____	12 – 8 = ____	18 – 8 = ____	9 – 8 = ____	14 – 8 = ____
15 – 8 = ____	15 – 8 = ____	11 – 8 = ____	10 – 8 = ____	13 – 8 = ____
11 – 8 = ____	9 – 8 = ____	10 – 8 = ____	8 – 8 = ____	16 – 8 = ____
12 – 8 = ____	13 – 8 = ____	15 – 8 = ____	14 – 8 = ____	18 – 8 = ____
17 – 8 = ____	17 – 8 = ____	9 – 8 = ____	13 – 8 = ____	11 – 8 = ____
14 – 8 = ____	11 – 8 = ____	16 – 8 = ____	15 – 8 = ____	9 – 8 = ____
13 – 8 = ____	10 – 8 = ____	17 – 8 = ____	16 – 8 = ____	15 – 8 = ____
16 – 8 = ____	18 – 8 = ____	14 – 8 = ____	9 – 8 = ____	10 – 8 = ____
18 – 8 = ____	16 – 8 = ____	12 – 8 = ____	12 – 8 = ____	16 – 8 = ____
15 – 8 = ____	12 – 8 = ____	8 – 8 = ____	11 – 8 = ____	13 – 8 = ____
9 – 8 = ____	15 – 8 = ____	11 – 8 = ____	17 – 8 = ____	14 – 8 = ____
10 – 8 = ____	9 – 8 = ____	13 – 8 = ____	18 – 8 = ____	12 – 8 = ____
11 – 8 = ____	14 – 8 = ____	10 – 8 = ____	10 – 8 = ____	17 – 8 = ____
14 – 8 = ____	8 – 8 = ____	9 – 8 = ____	15 – 8 = ____	15 – 8 = ____
12 – 8 = ____	13 – 8 = ____	12 – 8 = ____	13 – 8 = ____	10 – 8 = ____
17 – 8 = ____	10 – 8 = ____	18 – 8 = ____	14 – 8 = ____	9 – 8 = ____
8 – 8 = ____	11 – 8 = ____	16 – 8 = ____	12 – 8 = ____	11 – 8 = ____
13 – 8 = ____	17 – 8 = ____	13 – 8 = ____	16 – 8 = ____	8 – 8 = ____
Score: ____/25 ____ Min. ____ Sec.	Score: ____/25 ____ Min. ____ Sec.	Score: ____/25 ____ Min. ____ Sec.	Score: ____/25 ____ Min. ____ Sec.	Score: ____/25 ____ Min. ____ Sec.

Extra Practice Minus Eight Drills

Name: _____

Day 1	Day 2	Day 3	Day 4	Day 5
14 - ___ = 6	16 - ___ = 6	14 - 8 = ___	9 - 8 = ___	16 - 8 = ___
17 - 8 = ___	10 - ___ = 2	___ - 8 = 5	8 - ___ = 0	___ - 8 = 1
___ - 8 = 4	___ - 8 = 1	16 - ___ = 8	___ - 8 = 2	15 - ___ = 7
8 - ___ = 0	15 - ___ = 7	15 - 8 = ___	11 - 8 = ___	12 - 8 = ___
16 - 8 = ___	11 - ___ = 3	___ - 8 = 9	17 - ___ = 9	___ - 8 = 6
___ - 8 = 5	___ - 8 = 9	12 - 8 = ___	___ - 8 = 8	17 - ___ = 9
10 - ___ = 2	12 - ___ = 2	___ - 8 = 3	14 - 8 = ___	13 - 8 = ___
9 - 8 = ___	14 - 8 = ___	9 - ___ = 1	___ - 8 = 4	___ - 8 = 10
___ - 8 = 7	___ - 8 = 5	10 - 8 = ___	15 - ___ = 7	11 - ___ = 3
11 - ___ = 3	16 - 8 = ___	___ - 8 = 0	9 - ___ = 1	10 - 8 = ___
12 - 8 = ___	18 - ___ = 10	14 - 8 = ___	___ - 8 = 7	___ - 8 = 7
___ - 8 = 9	11 - 8 = ___	13 - ___ = 5	17 - 8 = ___	9 - ___ = 1
14 - ___ = 6	9 - ___ = 1	___ - 8 = 7	11 - ___ = 3	16 - 8 = ___
13 - 8 = ___	___ - 8 = 7	16 - 8 = ___	10 - 8 = ___	17 - ___ = 9
___ - 8 = 8	10 - 8 = ___	9 - ___ = 1	___ - 8 = 10	___ - 8 = 6
18 - ___ = 10	___ - 8 = 8	___ - 8 = 4	16 - ___ = 8	12 - 8 = ___
15 - 8 = ___	13 - ___ = 5	11 - 8 = ___	12 - 8 = ___	8 - ___ = 0
___ - 8 = 1	14 - 8 = ___	___ - 8 = 9	___ - 8 = ___	___ - 8 = 3
10 - ___ = 2	12 - ___ = 4	18 - ___ = 10	9 - ___ = 1	13 - 8 = ___
11 - 8 = ___	___ - 8 = 9	10 - 8 = ___	14 - 8 = ___	10 - ___ = 2
12 - ___ = 4	15 - 8 = ___	15 - ___ = 7	8 - ___ = 0	9 - ___ = 1
14 - 8 = ___	10 - 8 = ___	___ - 8 = 5	___ - 8 = 5	___ - 8 = 4
___ - 8 = 9	___ - 8 = 1	14 - ___ = 6	10 - 8 = ___	18 - ___ = 10
8 - ___ = 0	11 - ___ = 3	12 - 8 = ___	11 - ___ = 3	16 - 8 = ___
13 - 8 = ___	8 - 8 = ___	___ - 8 = 8	17 - 8 = ___	13 - ___ = 5
Score: _____ /25	Score: _____ /25	Score: _____ /25	Score: _____ /25	Score: _____ /25
_____ Min.	_____ Min.	_____ Min.	_____ Min.	_____ Min.
_____ Sec.	_____ Sec.	_____ Sec.	_____ Sec.	_____ Sec.

Minus Eight Drill Sheet Test

Name: _____

14 − 8	17 − 8	12 − 8	8 − 8	16 − 8	13 − 8	10 − 8	9 − 8	15 − 8	11 − 8
12 − 8	13 − 8	18 − 8	17 − 8	15 − 8	9 − 8	14 − 8	12 − 8	10 − 8	16 − 8
14 − 8	17 − 8	16 − 8	11 − 8	12 − 8	8 − 8	18 − 8	9 − 8	13 − 8	17 − 8
13 − 8	15 − 8	10 − 8	12 − 8	16 − 8	9 − 8	17 − 8	14 − 8	15 − 8	11 − 8
14 − 8	9 − 8	8 − 8	11 − 8	13 − 8	15 − 8	10 − 8	16 − 8	13 − 8	15 − 8
17 − 8	12 − 8	11 − 8	16 − 8	9 − 8	14 − 8	10 − 8	8 − 8	14 − 8	11 − 8
9 − 8	16 − 8	12 − 8	17 − 8	15 − 8	18 − 8	11 − 8	10 − 8	15 − 8	13 − 8
13 − 8	14 − 8	9 − 8	11 − 8	17 − 8	10 − 8	16 − 8	8 − 8	12 − 8	16 − 8
14 − 8	12 − 8	15 − 8	10 − 8	9 − 8	13 − 8	17 − 8	11 − 8	10 − 8	18 − 8
16 − 8	15 − 8	13 − 8	11 − 8	12 − 8	14 − 8	8 − 8	17 − 8	9 − 8	10 − 8

Date: _____ Score: _____/100 Time: _____ Min. _____ Sec.

Minus Nine Drills

Name: _____

Date: Monday _____ Score: _____/25 Time: _____ Min. _____ Sec.

14 – 9 = ____	13 – 9 = ____	12 – 9 = ____	18 – 9 = ____	14 – 9 = ____
17 – 9 = ____	10 – 9 = ____	17 – 9 = ____	15 – 9 = ____	12 – 9 = ____
12 – 9 = ____	9 – 9 = ____	14 – 9 = ____	9 – 9 = ____	17 – 9 = ____
18 – 9 = ____	15 – 9 = ____	13 – 9 = ____	10 – 9 = ____	18 – 9 = ____
16 – 9 = ____	11 – 9 = ____	16 – 9 = ____	11 – 9 = ____	13 – 9 = ____

Date: Tuesday _____ Score: _____/25 Time: _____ Min. _____ Sec.

16 – 9 = ____	17 – 9 = ____	18 – 9 = ____	16 – 9 = ____	15 – 9 = ____
10 – 9 = ____	12 – 9 = ____	11 – 9 = ____	13 – 9 = ____	10 – 9 = ____
9 – 9 = ____	14 – 9 = ____	9 – 9 = ____	14 – 9 = ____	9 – 9 = ____
15 – 9 = ____	13 – 9 = ____	15 – 9 = ____	12 – 9 = ____	11 – 9 = ____
11 – 9 = ____	16 – 9 = ____	10 – 9 = ____	17 – 9 = ____	18 – 9 = ____

Date: Wednesday _____ Score: _____/25 Time: _____ Min. _____ Sec.

14 – 9 = ____	12 – 9 = ____	14 – 9 = ____	12 – 9 = ____	15 – 9 = ____
13 – 9 = ____	11 – 9 = ____	13 – 9 = ____	11 – 9 = ____	13 – 9 = ____
16 – 9 = ____	9 – 9 = ____	15 – 9 = ____	17 – 9 = ____	14 – 9 = ____
15 – 9 = ____	10 – 9 = ____	16 – 9 = ____	18 – 9 = ____	12 – 9 = ____
17 – 9 = ____	18 – 9 = ____	9 – 9 = ____	10 – 9 = ____	16 – 9 = ____

Date: Thursday _____ Score: _____/25 Time: _____ Min. _____ Sec.

9 – 9 = ____	16 – 9 = ____	13 – 9 = ____	16 – 9 = ____	18 – 9 = ____
18 – 9 = ____	14 – 9 = ____	17 – 9 = ____	12 – 9 = ____	13 – 9 = ____
10 – 9 = ____	12 – 9 = ____	11 – 9 = ____	15 – 9 = ____	10 – 9 = ____
11 – 9 = ____	15 – 9 = ____	10 – 9 = ____	9 – 9 = ____	11 – 9 = ____
17 – 9 = ____	9 – 9 = ____	18 – 9 = ____	14 – 9 = ____	17 – 9 = ____

Date: Friday _____ Score: _____/25 Time: _____ Min. _____ Sec.

16 – 9 = ____	17 – 9 = ____	15 – 9 = ____	12 – 9 = ____	9 – 9 = ____
9 – 9 = ____	13 – 9 = ____	9 – 9 = ____	18 – 9 = ____	12 – 9 = ____
15 – 9 = ____	18 – 9 = ____	16 – 9 = ____	11 – 9 = ____	18 – 9 = ____
12 – 9 = ____	11 – 9 = ____	17 – 9 = ____	13 – 9 = ____	16 – 9 = ____
14 – 9 = ____	10 – 9 = ____	14 – 9 = ____	10 – 9 = ____	13 – 9 = ____

Home Practice Minus Nine Drills

Name: _____

Monday	Tuesday	Wednesday	Thursday	Friday
16 – 9 = ____	14 – 9 = ____	10 – 9 = ____	14 – 9 = ____	9 – 9 = ____
10 – 9 = ____	13 – 9 = ____	18 – 9 = ____	17 – 9 = ____	18 – 9 = ____
9 – 9 = ____	16 – 9 = ____	16 – 9 = ____	12 – 9 = ____	10 – 9 = ____
15 – 9 = ____	15 – 9 = ____	12 – 9 = ____	18 – 9 = ____	11 – 9 = ____
11 – 9 = ____	17 – 9 = ____	15 – 9 = ____	16 – 9 = ____	17 – 9 = ____
17 – 9 = ____	12 – 9 = ____	9 – 9 = ____	13 – 9 = ____	16 – 9 = ____
12 – 9 = ____	11 – 9 = ____	14 – 9 = ____	10 – 9 = ____	14 – 9 = ____
14 – 9 = ____	9 – 9 = ____	18 – 9 = ____	9 – 9 = ____	12 – 9 = ____
13 – 9 = ____	10 – 9 = ____	13 – 9 = ____	15 – 9 = ____	15 – 9 = ____
16 – 9 = ____	18 – 9 = ____	10 – 9 = ____	11 – 9 = ____	9 – 9 = ____
18 – 9 = ____	14 – 9 = ____	11 – 9 = ____	12 – 9 = ____	13 – 9 = ____
11 – 9 = ____	13 – 9 = ____	17 – 9 = ____	17 – 9 = ____	17 – 9 = ____
9 – 9 = ____	15 – 9 = ____	13 – 9 = ____	14 – 9 = ____	11 – 9 = ____
15 – 9 = ____	16 – 9 = ____	16 – 9 = ____	13 – 9 = ____	16 – 9 = ____
10 – 9 = ____	9 – 9 = ____	9 – 9 = ____	16 – 9 = ____	17 – 9 = ____
16 – 9 = ____	12 – 9 = ____	15 – 9 = ____	18 – 9 = ____	14 – 9 = ____
13 – 9 = ____	11 – 9 = ____	12 – 9 = ____	15 – 9 = ____	12 – 9 = ____
14 – 9 = ____	17 – 9 = ____	14 – 9 = ____	9 – 9 = ____	18 – 9 = ____
12 – 9 = ____	18 – 9 = ____	17 – 9 = ____	10 – 9 = ____	11 – 9 = ____
17 – 9 = ____	10 – 9 = ____	13 – 9 = ____	11 – 9 = ____	13 – 9 = ____
15 – 9 = ____	15 – 9 = ____	18 – 9 = ____	14 – 9 = ____	10 – 9 = ____
10 – 9 = ____	13 – 9 = ____	11 – 9 = ____	12 – 9 = ____	9 – 9 = ____
9 – 9 = ____	14 – 9 = ____	10 – 9 = ____	17 – 9 = ____	12 – 9 = ____
11 – 9 = ____	12 – 9 = ____	15 – 9 = ____	18 – 9 = ____	18 – 9 = ____
18 – 9 = ____	16 – 9 = ____	9 – 9 = ____	13 – 9 = ____	16 – 9 = ____
Score: ____/25 ____ Min. ____ Sec.	Score: ____/25 ____ Min. ____ Sec.	Score: ____/25 ____ Min. ____ Sec.	Score: ____/25 ____ Min. ____ Sec.	Score: ____/25 ____ Min. ____ Sec.

Extra Practice Minus Nine Drills

Name: _____

Day 1	Day 2	Day 3	Day 4	Day 5
14 - ___ = 5	16 - ___ = 7	14 - ___ = 5	9 - ___ = 0	___ - 9 = 7
___ - 9 = 8	___ - 9 = 1	___ - 9 = 13	___ - 9 = 9	9 - 9 = ___
12 - 9 = ___	9 - 9 = ___	16 - 9 = ___	10 - 9 = ___	15 - ___ = 6
18 - ___ = 9	15 - ___ = 6	15 - ___ = 6	11 - ___ = 9	12 - 9 = ___
___ - 9 = 7	___ - 9 = 2	___ - 9 = 8	___ - 9 = 8	___ - 9 = 5
13 - 9 = ___	17 - ___ = 8	12 - 9 = ___	16 - 9 = ___	17 - ___ = 8
10 - ___ = 1	12 - ___ = 3	11 - ___ = 2	14 - ___ = 5	13 - 9 = ___
___ - 9 = 0	___ - 9 = 5	___ - 9 = 10	___ - 9 = 3	18 - 9 = ___
15 - 9 = ___	13 - 9 = ___	10 - 9 = ___	15 - 9 = ___	___ - 9 = 2
11 - ___ = 2	16 - ___ = 7	18 - ___ = 9	9 - ___ = 0	10 - 9 = ___
___ - 9 = 3	___ - 9 = 9	___ - 9 = 5	___ - 9 = 5	15 - ___ = 6
17 - 9 = ___	11 - 9 = ___	13 - 9 = ___	17 - ___ = 8	___ - 9 = 0
14 - ___ = 5	9 - ___ = 0	15 - ___ = 6	11 - 9 = ___	___ - 9 = 7
___ - 9 = 4	___ - 9 = 6	___ - 9 = 7	10 - ___ = 1	17 - 9 = ___
16 - 9 = ___	10 - 9 = ___	9 - 9 = ___	___ - 9 = 9	14 - 9 = ___
18 - ___ = 9	16 - ___ = 7	12 - ___ = 3	16 - 9 = ___	___ - 9 = 3
___ - 9 = 6	___ - 9 = 5	___ - 2 = 9	12 - 9 = ___	18 - ___ = 9
9 - 9 = ___	14 - 9 = ___	17 - 9 = ___	___ - 9 = 6	11 - ___ = 9
10 - ___ = 1	___ - 9 = 3	18 - ___ = 9	9 - ___ = 0	13 - 9 = ___
___ - 9 = 2	17 - ___ = 8	___ - 9 = 1	14 - ___ = 5	10 - 9 = ___
14 - 9 = ___	15 - 9 = ___	15 - 9 = ___	18 - 9 = ___	9 - ___ = 0
12 - ___ = 3	___ - 9 = 1	13 - ___ = 4	13 - ___ = 9	12 - 9 = ___
___ - 9 = 8	9 - ___ = 0	___ - 9 = 5	___ - 9 = 1	___ - 9 = 9
18 - 9 = ___	11 - 9 = ___	12 - 9 = ___	11 - 9 = ___	___ - 9 = 7
13 - ___ = 4	___ - 9 = 9	16 - ___ = 7	17 - 9 = ___	13 - 9 = ___
Score: ___/25	Score: ___/25	Score: ___/25	Score: ___/25	Score: ___/25
___ Min.	___ Min.	___ Min.	___ Min.	___ Min.
___ Sec.	___ Sec.	___ Sec.	___ Sec.	___ Sec.

Minus Nine Drill Sheet Test

Name: _____

14 −9	17 −9	12 −9	18 −9	16 −9	13 −9	10 −9	9 −9	15 −9	11 −9
12 −9	14 −9	15 −9	17 −9	9 −9	11 −9	18 −9	14 −9	13 −9	16 −9
17 −9	18 −9	13 −9	10 −9	16 −9	12 −9	10 −9	9 −9	15 −9	11 −9
12 −9	14 −9	16 −9	17 −9	18 −9	11 −9	13 −9	16 −9	13 −9	10 −9
14 −9	12 −9	9 −9	10 −9	15 −9	9 −9	18 −9	17 −9	16 −9	11 −9
11 −9	10 −9	12 −9	18 −9	17 −9	13 −9	15 −9	9 −9	14 −9	15 −9
13 −9	15 −9	9 −9	14 −9	12 −9	11 −9	16 −9	17 −9	18 −9	10 −9
14 −9	12 −9	16 −9	18 −9	10 −9	15 −9	17 −9	11 −9	9 −9	13 −9
16 −9	14 −9	15 −9	9 −9	12 −9	13 −9	11 −9	10 −9	18 −9	17 −9
9 −9	18 −9	13 −9	16 −9	10 −9	14 −9	17 −9	12 −9	16 −9	15 −9

Date: _____   Score: _____ /100   Time: _____ Min. _____ Sec.

–6, –7, –8, –9 Timed Drill Test

Name: _____

Row 1	Row 2	Row 3	Row 4
9 – 6 = _____	17 – 9 = _____	7 – 6 = _____	7 – 7 = _____
11 – 8 = _____	18 – 7 = _____	17 – 8 = _____	17 – 6 = _____
12 – 9 = _____	12 – 6 = _____	10 – 9 = _____	10 – 8 = _____
7 – 7 = _____	15 – 8 = _____	17 – 7 = _____	13 – 9 = _____
11 – 6 = _____	9 – 9 = _____	12 – 6 = _____	12 – 7 = _____
8 – 8 = _____	17 – 7 = _____	9 – 8 = _____	9 – 6 = _____
14 – 9 = _____	14 – 6 = _____	12 – 9 = _____	12 – 8 = _____
12 – 7 = _____	18 – 8 = _____	9 – 7 = _____	15 – 9 = _____
6 – 6 = _____	11 – 9 = _____	14 – 6 = _____	14 – 7 = _____
10 – 8 = _____	9 – 7 = _____	11 – 8 = _____	11 – 6 = _____
16 – 9 = _____	16 – 6 = _____	14 – 9 = _____	14 – 8 = _____
14 – 7 = _____	17 – 8 = _____	11 – 7 = _____	18 – 9 = _____
8 – 6 = _____	10 – 9 = _____	16 – 6 = _____	16 – 7 = _____
12 – 8 = _____	11 – 7 = _____	8 – 8 = _____	6 – 6 = _____
13 – 9 = _____	13 – 6 = _____	16 – 9 = _____	16 – 8 = _____
16 – 7 = _____	9 – 8 = _____	8 – 7 = _____	17 – 9 = _____
10 – 6 = _____	12 – 9 = _____	13 – 6 = _____	13 – 7 = _____
14 – 8 = _____	8 – 7 = _____	10 – 8 = _____	8 – 6 = _____
15 – 9 = _____	15 – 6 = _____	13 – 9 = _____	13 – 8 = _____
13 – 7 = _____	11 – 8 = _____	10 – 7 = _____	9 – 9 = _____
7 – 6 = _____	14 – 9 = _____	15 – 6 = _____	15 – 7 = _____
16 – 8 = _____	10 – 7 = _____	12 – 8 = _____	10 – 6 = _____
18 – 9 = _____	18 – 6 = _____	15 – 9 = _____	15 – 8 = _____
15 – 7 = _____	8 – 8 = _____	11 – 7 = _____	11 – 9 = _____
13 – 8 = _____	16 – 9 = _____	18 – 6 = _____	18 – 7 = _____

Date: _____   Score: _____/100   Time: _____ Min. _____ Sec.

–6, –7, –8, –9 Timed Drill Test

Name: _____

9 – 6	11 – 8	12 – 9	7 – 7	11 – 6	8 – 8	14 – 9	12 – 7	6 – 6	10 – 8
16 – 9	14 – 7	8 – 6	12 – 8	13 – 9	16 – 7	10 – 6	14 – 8	15 – 9	13 – 7
7 – 6	16 – 8	18 – 9	15 – 7	13 – 8	17 – 9	18 – 7	12 – 6	15 – 8	9 – 9
17 – 7	14 – 6	11 – 9	9 – 7	18 – 8	16 – 6	17 – 8	10 – 7	11 – 7	13 – 6
9 – 8	12 – 9	8 – 7	15 – 6	11 – 8	14 – 9	10 – 7	18 – 6	8 – 8	16 – 9
7 – 7	17 – 6	10 – 8	13 – 9	12 – 7	9 – 6	12 – 8	15 – 9	14 – 7	11 – 6
14 – 8	18 – 9	16 – 7	6 – 6	16 – 8	17 – 9	13 – 7	8 – 6	13 – 8	9 – 9
15 – 7	10 – 9	15 – 8	11 – 9	18 – 7	7 – 6	17 – 8	10 – 9	17 – 7	12 – 6
9 – 8	12 – 9	9 – 7	14 – 6	11 – 8	14 – 9	11 – 7	16 – 9	8 – 7	13 – 6
10 – 8	13 – 9	10 – 7	15 – 6	12 – 8	15 – 9	11 – 7	18 – 6	13 – 7	14 – 6

Date: _____   Score: _____ /100   Time: _____ Min. _____ Sec.

Review Drill of Subtraction Facts 0 to 18

Name: _____

A	8 −2	13 −8	6 −0	10 −8	5 −1	16 −9	8 −8	14 −5	1 −0	9 −7
B	10 −9	9 −6	4 −3	13 −7	2 −0	15 −8	7 −7	11 −8	8 −6	6 −3
C	12 −7	1 −1	10 −1	9 −8	7 −3	15 −7	9 −1	5 −0	14 −7	6 −2
D	8 −0	2 −1	15 −9	9 −3	11 −4	5 −3	14 −6	12 −9	6 −5	11 −7
E	6 −6	10 −6	12 −4	3 −0	17 −9	10 −3	4 −1	13 −9	9 −2	7 −4
F	4 −0	16 −7	7 −6	13 −4	5 −5	12 −3	10 −2	8 −5	3 −2	10 −7
G	4 −2	15 −6	9 −4	7 −0	12 −5	11 −2	0 −0	10 −4	13 −5	8 −1
H	9 −5	6 −4	11 −9	4 −4	18 −9	8 −4	2 −2	14 −9	7 −2	11 −5
I	6 −1	11 −6	8 −7	13 −6	3 −3	17 −8	10 −5	7 −5	12 −6	5 −2
J	9 −0	7 −1	14 −8	5 −4	12 −8	9 −9	8 −3	16 −8	3 −1	11 −3

Date: _____   Score: _____ /100   Time: _____ Min. _____ Sec.

© On The Mark Press • S&S Learning Materials   OTM-1140 • SSK1-40 Timed Subtraction Facts

Review Drill of Subtraction Facts 0 to 18

Name: _____

A	10 − 1	6 − 3	1 − 1	13 − 4	8 − 2	5 − 3	11 − 5	14 − 8	9 − 6	3 − 2
B	2 − 0	9 − 2	8 − 1	16 − 8	6 − 6	4 − 0	13 − 7	11 − 4	5 − 5	7 − 6
C	8 − 3	3 − 3	14 − 9	11 − 2	9 − 0	15 − 8	7 − 2	10 − 3	8 − 4	12 − 4
D	7 − 4	9 − 9	6 − 2	9 − 3	3 − 1	11 − 9	8 − 6	15 − 6	5 − 2	13 − 9
E	5 − 4	12 − 9	9 − 8	6 − 5	8 − 0	4 − 3	14 − 7	11 − 8	3 − 0	6 − 1
F	12 − 8	4 − 1	12 − 3	10 − 5	13 − 8	7 − 0	12 − 7	2 − 1	18 − 9	9 − 1
G	10 − 7	8 − 5	5 − 0	9 − 5	14 − 5	7 − 3	1 − 0	12 − 6	10 − 4	17 − 9
H	0 − 0	14 − 6	11 − 3	12 − 5	17 − 8	9 − 7	15 − 7	13 − 6	8 − 8	15 − 9
I	7 − 7	10 − 6	4 − 4	11 − 6	6 − 4	10 − 9	16 − 7	6 − 0	16 − 9	7 − 5
J	7 − 1	10 − 2	5 − 1	9 − 4	4 − 2	13 − 5	8 − 7	11 − 7	2 − 2	10 − 8

Date: _____   Score: _____ /100   Time: _____ Min. _____ Sec.

Review Drill of Subtraction Facts 0 to 18

Name: _____

A	13 – 4 = ____	2 – 0 = ____	10 – 3 = ____	9 – 6 = ____	11 – 4 = ____
B	6 – 3 = ____	12 – 3 = ____	8 – 6 = ____	16 – 9 = ____	7 – 3 = ____
C	11 – 2 = ____	4 – 1 = ____	10 – 2 = ____	7 – 7 = ____	16 – 7 = ____
D	2 – 1 = ____	11 – 7 = ____	6 – 1 = ____	14 – 9 = ____	7 – 5 = ____
E	11 – 5 = ____	7 – 2 = ____	13 – 7 = ____	6 – 5 = ____	14 – 6 = ____
F	3 – 3 = ____	15 – 7 = ____	9 – 3 = ____	11 – 9 = ____	1 – 0 = ____
G	12 – 8 = ____	8 – 4 = ____	9 – 7 = ____	6 – 3 = ____	13 – 5 = ____
H	9 – 0 = ____	18 – 9 = ____	5 – 4 = ____	10 – 6 = ____	8 – 1 = ____
I	10 – 8 = ____	8 – 3 = ____	15 – 9 = ____	5 – 3 = ____	17 – 8 = ____
J	9 – 1 = ____	10 – 7 = ____	3 – 0 = ____	14 – 5 = ____	5 – 2 = ____
K	15 – 9 = ____	8 – 8 = ____	14 – 8 = ____	6 – 2 = ____	13 – 9 = ____
L	9 – 5 = ____	10 – 9 = ____	7 – 0 = ____	12 – 5 = ____	3 – 2 = ____
M	10 – 5 = ____	4 – 0 = ____	12 – 4 = ____	7 – 4 = ____	12 – 7 = ____
N	0 – 0 = ____	9 – 8 = ____	7 – 1 = ____	13 – 6 = ____	4 – 2 = ____
O	10 – 4 = ____	8 – 2 = ____	17 – 9 = ____	5 – 1 = ____	10 – 1 = ____
P	9 – 2 = ____	15 – 2 = ____	4 – 4 = ____	9 – 9 = ____	8 – 1 = ____
Q	1 – 1 = ____	6 – 4 = ____	11 – 8 = ____	4 – 3 = ____	3 – 1 = ____
R	8 – 5 = ____	12 – 9 = ____	5 – 5 = ____	11 – 3 = ____	7 – 6 = ____
S	12 – 6 = ____	2 – 2 = ____	16 – 8 = ____	9 – 4 = ____	14 – 7 = ____
T	5 – 0 = ____	13 – 8 = ____	8 – 7 = ____	11 – 6 = ____	6 – 6 = ____

Date: _____   Score: _____ /100   Time: _____ Min. _____ Sec.

Review Drill of Subtraction Facts 0 to 18

Name: _____

A	11 – 9 = ____	6 – 1 = ____	12 – 8 = ____	9 – 7 = ____	4 – 1 = ____
B	11 – 2 = ____	16 – 9 = ____	7 – 2 = ____	5 – 4 = ____	10 – 1 = ____
C	13 – 6 = ____	2 – 2 = ____	12 – 5 = ____	7 – 4 = ____	10 – 6 = ____
D	8 – 4 = ____	14 – 8 = ____	6 – 5 = ____	3 – 0 = ____	9 – 4 = ____
E	10 – 5 = ____	7 – 6 = ____	2 – 1 = ____	15 – 9 = ____	6 – 4 = ____
F	11 – 8 = ____	10 – 8 = ____	0 – 0 = ____	17 – 9 = ____	4 – 4 = ____
G	8 – 7 = ____	9 – 5 = ____	14 – 5 = ____	4 – 0 = ____	17 – 8 = ____
H	9 – 1 = ____	6 – 0 = ____	11 – 6 = ____	12 – 3 = ____	5 – 1 = ____
I	3 – 3 = ____	13 – 9 = ____	5 – 0 = ____	12 – 6 = ____	11 – 4 = ____
J	8 – 2 = ____	15 – 7 = ____	6 – 3 = ____	9 – 2 = ____	13 – 4 = ____
K	6 – 6 = ____	18 – 9 = ____	8 – 5 = ____	16 – 7 = ____	1 – 1 = ____
L	10 – 3 = ____	15 – 8 = ____	8 – 0 = ____	7 – 3 = ____	10 – 9 = ____
M	9 – 8 = ____	5 – 5 = ____	13 – 5 = ____	9 – 3 = ____	1 – 0 = ____
N	13 – 8 = ____	7 – 5 = ____	12 – 4 = ____	10 – 4 = ____	3 – 1 = ____
O	11 – 7 = ____	7 – 0 = ____	9 – 0 = ____	15 – 6 = ____	5 – 2 = ____
P	12 – 7 = ____	13 – 7 = ____	8 – 8 = ____	14 – 7 = ____	4 – 2 = ____
Q	7 – 1 = ____	10 – 2 = ____	11 – 5 = ____	3 – 2 = ____	8 – 3 = ____
R	14 – 1 = ____	9 – 6 = ____	5 – 3 = ____	8 – 1 = ____	10 – 7 = ____
S	4 – 3 = ____	11 – 3 = ____	2 – 0 = ____	9 – 9 = ____	12 – 9 = ____
T	8 – 6 = ____	6 – 2 = ____	16 – 8 = ____	7 – 7 = ____	14 – 9 = ____

Date: _____   Score: _____/100   Time: _____ Min. _____ Sec.

Score Record Sheet for _____ **Drills**
Name: _____

1. Date: _____
   Score: ___/25 Time: ___Min. ___Sec.

2. Date: _____
   Score: ___/25 Time: ___Min. ___Sec.

3. Date: _____
   Score: ___/25 Time: ___Min. ___Sec.

4. Date: _____
   Score: ___/25 Time: ___Min. ___Sec.

5. Date: _____
   Score: ___/25 Time: ___Min. ___Sec.

6. Date: _____
   Score: ___/25 Time: ___Min. ___Sec.

7. Date: _____
   Score: ___/25 Time: ___Min. ___Sec.

8. Date: _____
   Score: ___/25 Time: ___Min. ___Sec.

9. Date: _____
   Score: ___/25 Time: ___Min. ___Sec.

10. Date: _____
    Score: ___/25 Time: ___Min. ___Sec.

11. Date: _____
    Score: ___/25 Time: ___Min. ___Sec.

12. Date: _____
    Score: ___/25 Time: ___Min. ___Sec.

My speed and accuracy is
_____ .

Score Record Sheet for _____ **Drills**
Name: _____

1. Date: _____
   Score: ___/100 Time: ___Min. ___Sec.

2. Date: _____
   Score: ___/100 Time: ___Min. ___Sec.

3. Date: _____
   Score: ___/100 Time: ___Min. ___Sec.

4. Date: _____
   Score: ___/100 Time: ___Min. ___Sec.

5. Date: _____
   Score: ___/100 Time: ___Min. ___Sec.

6. Date: _____
   Score: ___/100 Time: ___Min. ___Sec.

7. Date: _____
   Score: ___/100 Time: ___Min. ___Sec.

8. Date: _____
   Score: ___/100 Time: ___Min. ___Sec.

9. Date: _____
   Score: ___/100 Time: ___Min. ___Sec.

10. Date: _____
    Score: ___/100 Time: ___Min. ___Sec.

11. Date: _____
    Score: ___/100 Time: ___Min. ___Sec.

12. Date: _____
    Score: ___/100 Time: ___Min. ___Sec.

My speed and accuracy is
_____ .